The Open University

Water for life

1

Photos on title page   Two organisms that can survive in regions where water is scarce: Arabian camels and barrel cacti.

The Open University, Walton Hall, Milton Keynes MK7 6AA

First published 1997. Reprinted 1999, 2001

Written, edited, designed and typeset by The Open University.

Printed and bound in Singapore under the supervision of MRM Graphic Ltd, Winslow, Bucks.

ISBN 0 7492 8187 1

This text forms part of an Open University Level One Course. If you would like a copy of *Studying with The Open University*, please write to the Course Enquiries Data Service, P. O. Box 625, Dane Road, Milton Keynes MK1 1TY, United Kingdom. If you have not enrolled on the Course and would like to buy this or other Open University material, please write to Open University Educational Enterprises Ltd, 12 Cofferidge Close, Stony Stratford, Milton Keynes MK11 1BY, United Kingdom.

s103block1i1.3

Contents

Introduction

1

Have you ever asked yourself why ice floats on the surface of a pond rather than sinking to the bottom, or why sweating can cool you down? Have you ever wondered how camels can survive for long periods in the desert without water but humans cannot? These questions are all related to the theme of this introductory block, *Water for life*.

We've chosen to start *Discovering Science* with this topic for a variety of reasons. First of all, it allows us to introduce some fascinating science, spanning the four main areas of science covered in this course — biology, chemistry, Earth sciences and physics. Water is essential for life, and without water there would be no life. Water also has many special properties that single it out from other substances, and that make it of interest to scientists in all areas.

A second reason for choosing the theme *Water for life* is that both water and life are subjects that are part of your everyday experience; you know a lot about them already. For example, water is the most common liquid on the Earth; it forms ice; it falls in the form of rain; all plants and animals need water to survive, and so on. This knowledge provides a foundation on which you can build in this introductory block and in the rest of the course.

Water for life is a huge theme, and it would be possible to write a whole course that focused on this one subject. However, our goal in this introductory block is not to be comprehensive. We have selected a range of topics, from the use of water by individuals in the United Kingdom (UK)* to the threat of water pollution on a world-wide scale, and from how desert organisms survive arid conditions to the survival of plants and fish in ponds in freezing conditions.

Section 2 looks at how water is used in the UK and considers why water is important for life. Section 3 explores the amount of water in different organisms and how organisms that live in deserts manage to survive. We usually think of water as a liquid but it can also occur as ice and as water vapour, and Section 4 considers some of the properties of these three forms of water and their relevance for living organisms. Section 5 takes a break from the main theme of the block and introduces writing skills that are important for communicating your understanding of science to others. You will put these skills into practice while studying Section 6, which looks at how human societies exploit water and considers some of the consequences of this for the environment. The block concludes with a brief discussion of the activities and responsibilities of scientists, and in so doing looks at what 'science' is all about.

As well as exploring topics related to the theme *Water for life*, you will be developing a number of essential skills. These include: organizing and planning your study time; reading this book 'actively' and writing your responses to questions and activities; learning to use other study materials, such as videocassettes; and learning and revising maths skills, including the use of a calculator.

Where you concentrate your main efforts while studying this block will depend on your current strengths and weaknesses. You may have left school with a dislike of mathematics and with no maths qualifications; if so, you'll need to spend a

*The United Kingdom is the political entity of England, Northern Ireland, Scotland and Wales.

considerable amount of time working through the maths and calculator sections. But if you have already done a lot of maths and are skilled at using a calculator, you can read through those sections quite quickly and try a couple of questions to check your understanding. However, although you may be pretty competent at maths, you may not be too good when it comes to written communication; if that is the case, you'll need to study the sections relating to communication quite carefully. If this is your first Open University course, then you will need to spend a fair amount of time planning how to organize your time and your study materials, and trying out different strategies for learning from the various course materials, and we've provided a range of activities that will help you with this.

To get you started on thinking about some practical arrangements for studying, try Activity 1.1.

Activity 1.1   Preparing for study

Before you move on to Section 2, spend a few minutes thinking about (a) where you will study, and (b) where you will keep your Open University materials. ◀

The activities in this course require you to break off study of the text and do something; for example, carry out some practical work, watch a video or write a response in your Study File. An icon in the margin of the book indicates the type of activity and ◀ indicates the end of the activity. The Study File contains *notes* to help you with these activities, so you should always refer to the Study File before starting the activity. The Study File also contains *comments*, which should always be read *after* attempting the activity for yourself.

Life in the desert?

2

The title of this book may have conjured up a variety of images in your mind when you first saw it, but the image in Figure 2.1 was unlikely to have been one of them. These dry bones, which were excavated in a desert location, give the very opposite impression to 'water for life'. But this contrast serves to emphasize that life, in all its known forms, is critically dependent on the presence of water. Where there is no water present, there is no life.

In this section we shall start our exploration of the theme *Water for life* by considering how the bones in Figure 2.1 came to be in this inhospitable desert location, where very little water is available. We shall then show how the distribution of the world's population is related to the availability of water, discuss the pattern of water use in the UK, and look at different water-based fluids essential to keep the human body functioning properly.

Note the convention for numbering figures, tables, questions and activities in this course. The first number refers to the section in which it appears; the second number to the order within that section. For example, Figure 2.1 is the first figure in Section 2; Activity 3.2 is the second activity in Section 3.

Figure 2.1   The skeleton of an adolescent female discovered during excavation of a ruined town in the Egyptian Sahara Desert.

The focus in this section is not on introducing you to new science, but on introducing a number of skills that you will find invaluable as you study *Discovering Science*. Among these skills are reading information from diagrams and tables, as well as from printed words, and using a calculator for arithmetic and for working out percentages. We shall also encourage you to think about how you plan your study time.

Activity 2.1   Monitoring your study

Finding time to study is a major challenge for Open University students, but planning when and how to study is difficult until you've actually tried tackling some course material. So as a first stage in developing study planning skills, you should use the timetable grid for Activity 2.1 in the Study File to keep a log of the time you spend studying Section 2. When you have completed the section we shall ask you to review the time you have spent on it and this will help you plan how much time to set aside for future sections. ◀

2.1 Bones in the desert

The bones shown in the photograph in Figure 2.1 were discovered in the early 1980s by a French archaeological team when excavating a ruined town in the Egyptian Sahara Desert. The skeleton is that of an adolescent girl who was alive about 4 000 years ago, and we'll give her the name Bones to make it easier to refer to her later. As Figure 2.2 shows, the Sahara region is now an arid desert; there is no vegetation in sight. This is the driest part of the Sahara, with perhaps one or two centimetres of rain in a year.

Figure 2.2 Parched desert landscape in the Egyptian Sahara Desert. When the large stone was overturned, two smaller stones were discovered, which had been used for grinding grain about 4 500 years before Bones was born.

The numbered questions should help you to consolidate your understanding of the text you have just read and so should be tackled when you come to them. You should write your answer either in the margin of this book or on a separate sheet of paper in your Study File before referring to the answer and comments at the end of this book. (Answers to numbered questions begin on p. 100.)

Question 2.1 One of the things you will need to do as a scientist is to ask questions. Suppose that *you* had discovered Bones in her resting place, which is now a desert. Make a note of some questions that you would like answered to satisfy your curiosity about how Bones came to be in the place where she was found. ◄

Before reading on, check your answer to Question 2.1 against ours.

Asking questions is an important step in the process of discovering more about the world around us. Your questions, and our list of some possible questions in the answer and comments on Question 2.1, may well include questions that would occur to an archaeologist who unearthed a skeleton like Bones. Archaeology is the scientific study of human antiquities, and archaeologists share many of the same scientific methods of working as the biologists, chemists, Earth scientists and physicists who will figure much more prominently in this course.

An archaeologist might think of a number of possible explanations to account for how the skeleton came to be in the desert location where it was discovered. Here are two possibilities.

1   At the time when Bones was living, the area had sufficient rainfall to support a flourishing community that grew all of their own food. Since that time, the climate has changed and the area has become desert, so that it is now impossible to cultivate crops and the area is uninhabited.

2   The area had a desert climate at the time Bones lived there, but she was part of an advanced civilization that developed an irrigation system for agriculture. The irrigation system began to fall into disrepair, so that agricultural production collapsed and the population migrated away.

Now these are very different explanations and there are various other possibilities, but it is probable that an archaeologist would have reasons to prefer some of them rather than others. It is likely that there would be a body of existing knowledge that could be used to rule out some possibilities. For example, previous excavations nearby might have provided evidence of the type of climate at around the time that Bones was living. However, there may well be several possible explanations that are consistent with existing knowledge, and the archaeologist would then look for new evidence that supported or disproved these explanations.

⬤   What evidence might an archaeologist look for to support or disprove either of the two explanations listed above?

◯   Evidence from excavations might indicate the type of houses that were built at the time Bones lived, which might provide clues to the climate. The nature of any items found, such as tools or pottery, would provide information about how advanced the civilization was. Excavations might also provide evidence for irrigation systems. In addition, excavations could be undertaken specifically to look for evidence of animal and plant life, and if such evidence were found it might indicate whether or not there had always been a desert climate in the area.

There have been extensive archaeological excavations in the Egyptian Sahara, and they have allowed archaeologists to build up a fascinating picture of the area. Of particular interest in the context of our 'water for life' theme is the fact that the Sahara has not always been a desert! If you go back 20 000 years, to a time when northwest Europe was covered under a thick ice sheet, then the Sahara was rich grassland that provided hunting grounds for prehistoric people. Stone tools from this period have been found in the desert, as well as remnants of ostrich eggs and evidence of early farming. However, about 10 000 years ago, as the Earth warmed and as the ice receded from Europe, the climate of North Africa changed to become the hot dry desert climate with which we are now familiar. The human and animal populations either moved north to the Mediterranean coast, east to the Nile valley, or south, in each case to regions where water was available. The once rich grassland was replaced by barren desert, punctuated in places by oases, where underground water allowed date palms and fruit trees to grow. It was in such an oasis that Bones' town flourished 4 200 years ago.

The research that established Bones' background illustrates the **scientific method**, a term used to describe the way that knowledge and understanding advance in a wide range of scientific subjects. An archaeological discovery, such as the unearthing of Bones or the town where she was found, would generally be a new piece of information that had to be fitted into a jigsaw puzzle of existing knowledge about early civilizations in that area. This could lead archaeologists to develop a **hypothesis**, a tentative explanation, based on the available evidence, of the part Bones and the town played in those civilizations. In order to test the hypothesis, they would look for further evidence about Bones, possibly by more excavations at the same site or at a different site, or by making some scientific measurements on the bones or objects found at the site. Subsequent discoveries might confirm part or all of the initial hypothesis, and might allow the hypothesis to be developed further. On the

Questions like this are designed to make you stop and think about what you are reading and help you progress to the next step. The answer follows on immediately, so you can reassure yourself that you are following the argument. However, you will get the most out of the text if you cover the answer while you try to answer the question for yourself.

In this paragraph two terms appear in **bold**. These are terms that we expect you to be able to explain the meaning of, and use correctly, both during your study of the course and at the end of the course. You will find definitions of these terms in the Glossary.

other hand, new evidence might cause the archaeologists to make some changes, or modifications, to their hypothesis, or even to reject the initial hypothesis and replace it by a completely new one. For example, new evidence about burial rituals might suggest that Bones had died elsewhere and been moved to the burial place where she was found.

Archaeologists now have a great deal of confidence in their current hypothesis: the ruined town flourished in a desert oasis in Ancient Egypt's Sixth Dynasty, about 4 200 years ago. However, it is always possible that some important future find, or some re-evaluation of previous work, will make archaeologists modify the hypothesis, or even reject it in favour of a completely different hypothesis. This constant process of re-evaluation is a characteristic of the world of science, and scientists should always be open to the possibility that new experiments, observations or discoveries may overthrow even a highly favoured hypothesis. That's one of the reasons that science is so exciting!

2.2   People don't live in deserts

The need for water to maintain human life, both for essential drinking water and for cultivating food, means that human populations in desert areas are generally very low. Populations are very much higher where there are plentiful supplies of water. This is evident from comparing the two maps in Figure 2.3, but before you do this have a look at Box 2.1, *Reading illustrations*, which introduces an important skill for studying science.

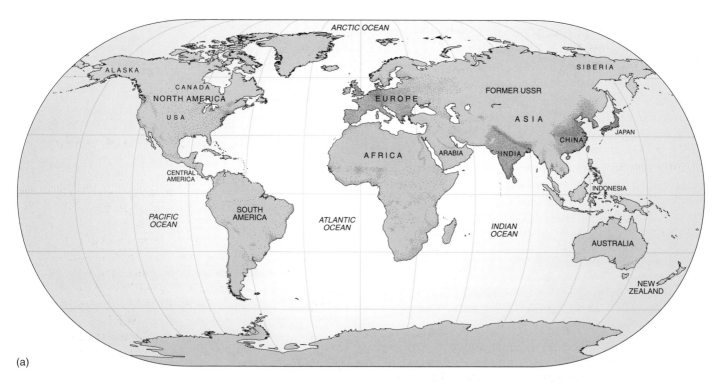

(a)

Figure 2.3   (a) A map of the world showing the distribution of the human population; each dot represents the same number of people. (b) A map showing world rainfall; the annual rainfall in different areas is indicated by the colour, and the meaning of each colour is shown in the key.

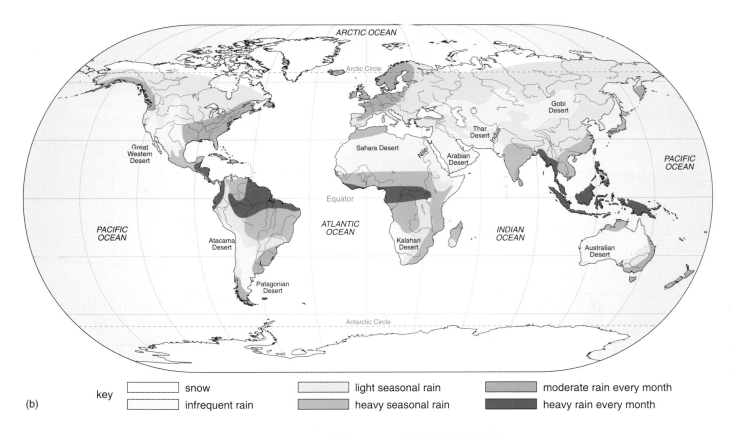

key ☐ snow   ☐ light seasonal rain   ▨ moderate rain every month
     ☐ infrequent rain   ▨ heavy seasonal rain   ■ heavy rain every month

(b)

Boxes are used where we break off from the main theme. Sometimes they introduce new maths or a new science skill. Other times they contain important supplementary material, such as a snippet of interesting science, that consolidates your understanding of the text. The best time to study a box is when you are first referred to it.

Box 2.1   Reading illustrations

Recall for a moment the last time you read a paperback novel. Almost certainly it consisted of a few hundred pages of print, unbroken by any illustrations. Not all books are like that, of course. For example, both cookery books and do-it-yourself manuals are usually well illustrated by photographs, drawings, diagrams, etc.

● The illustrations in these two types of book usually serve very different purposes. Can you think what these are?

○ Those in a cookery book are largely to make the book look more interesting and to tempt you. They are normally photographs of a finished dish at its mouth-watering best. Those in a do-it-yourself manual are normally designed to help you see how to carry out a particular task.

The first two illustrations you have met in this section (Figures 2.1 and 2.2) come into the category of 'largely for interest'. They are there to lend some sense of reality to the notion of human bones found in a desert, and to break up a page or so of printed text. Figure 2.3 is different. It conveys important information and is an integral part of the teaching of Section 2.2, and this is why you will be asked to do some work on it. Most of the illustrations in this book, and in other scientific texts you will read, serve this purpose. You will not be asked to do some work on every illustration you meet, but you will be expected to 'read' all of them in order to understand how they are clarifying or adding to what you are reading in the text.

Most of the illustrations have a *figure number* for identification and ease of reference — it's 2.3 for the maps that precede this box. As you read the text you will find a reference to the figure number, and that is the best point at which to examine the figure. Along with the figure number there will be a *figure caption* (or title); this explains what the illustration is showing, and the caption is the best place to start 'reading' the illustration. So for Figure 2.3, the caption first tells us that there are two parts to the figure, (a) and (b), and they are maps that show world population distribution and world rainfall, respectively. It also tells us something about how these quantities are represented on the maps.

As you will appreciate, because the Earth is a sphere the views you are shown in Figure 2.3 are not those you would see if you could look down on the Earth from space. Figure 6.1 (Section 6) is an example of a view from a satellite, and it shows only the part of the Earth that was facing the satellite when the photograph was taken. The advantage of maps like those shown in Figure 2.3 is that they allow us to present the whole surface of the Earth in one picture. Scientists often use diagrams to represent particular aspects of an object, and these diagrams are rarely accurate representations of all aspects of the object. The population map, for example, shows the world as a flat sheet, with Alaska a long way from Siberia, whereas a look at a globe will show that they are close together. However, as long as we bear in mind the limitations of this sort of map, it is a very useful way to convey information about the population of all regions of the world in a single diagram.

Figure 2.3a shows how densely populated the different areas of the Earth are. The population information is conveyed by the dots on the map, and the caption tells us that each dot represents the same number of people. This means that where the dots are very close together, then more people live in that region. In other words, there is a high *population density* in that region. England, for example, has a high population density overall, and the dots are close together there. If you live in a rural area you may find this concept hard to comprehend, but the low population density in the countryside is balanced by a far higher population density in cities and towns. To read Figure 2.3a in the context of Section 2.2, you don't need to know how many people each dot represents. All you need to know is that the more dots there are in a given area, the more densely populated that area is. The impact is immediate.

○ From Figure 2.3a, which are the most densely populated areas of the world?

○ You should have picked India, China, Japan and Europe (including the UK). It is in these areas that the dots are the closest together.

Figure 2.3b shows how rainfall (or snowfall) varies in different regions of the world. This time there is a *key* to show you what the different colours on the map mean. Hot desert areas where it seldom rains are coloured yellow, and areas where there is heavy rainfall throughout the year are dark blue.

○ Consider the visual impact of Figure 2.3b. Do you think the colours used were chosen arbitrarily?

○ No, the colours have associations for us. Blue is traditionally the colour of the sea, a watery environment: the darker the blue, the more watery the environment. Yellow is the colour of sand, which we associate with deserts. Because of these sorts of associations, it is easy to distinguish at a glance the wet areas from the dry areas.

We have labelled three features in Figure 2.3b that were not labelled in Figure 2.3a. These are the locations of the Equator and the Arctic and Antarctic Circles. They were not labelled on Figure 2.3a because they were irrelevant to our discussion of the world population distribution. However, they are relevant to our consideration of world rainfall and deserts. You probably associate the Arctic Circle with cold temperatures, and the Equator with hot temperatures. The closer to the Equator you go, in general, the higher the average annual temperatures and so the more likely you are to find hot deserts if there is little rain. Beyond the Arctic Circle, you are likely to experience snowfall rather than rainfall. Both maps show some lines of latitude and longitude, and we shall be discussing these in Block 2.

Later in this book we will explore the function of illustrations a little more. In the meantime, as you encounter each new illustration you should stop to think about its function (is it largely for interest or is it an integral part of the teaching?), and you should try to jot down, either in the margin of the book or in your Study File, the important points that you read from it.

We said at the start of Section 2.2 that the populations in desert areas are generally very low. Let's regard this as an initial hypothesis, and see if it is supported by evidence from the maps in Figure 2.3. Figure 2.3a shows how densely populated the different areas of the Earth are. If you look at this map, you will see that there are many areas where there are practically no dots at all, indicating that there are very, very few people living there.

- Do these areas of low population density coincide with any of the desert areas that you know of?

- There is clearly a low population density indicated for North Africa, and this corresponds to the location of the Sahara Desert. Another low population density area is shown in Australia, where there are also large regions of desert. You may have identified others.

This information clearly supports our initial hypothesis, but let's look a bit further. Figure 2.3b allows you to make a comparison between population density and rainfall. Hot desert areas where it seldom rains are coloured yellow, and the names of many of the deserts are shown. Many of these areas are located in two bands on either side of the Equator.

- Does a comparison of the two maps in Figure 2.3 confirm that very few people live in these hot desert areas? Are there any exceptions?

- Desert areas shown in the map in Figure 2.3b generally match up with the low population density areas shown in Figure 2.3a. Two clear exceptions that you might have noticed are along the Nile river valley in Egypt, and along the Indus river valley in Pakistan.

The Nile and Indus valleys have desert climates with little rainfall. The large rivers that give their names to these valleys bring water from the mountains, which can be used for drinking, crop irrigation, and so on, so that high populations can be supported in these areas. We, therefore, need to modify our initial hypothesis, and a revised hypothesis is that *populations in desert areas are very low unless abundant sources of water are available from outside the region.*

The procedure that we have just followed illustrates the scientific method (introduced in Section 2.1). We made an initial hypothesis based on a few observations; we tested this hypothesis by making further observations; and we then revised our hypothesis to make it consistent with all of the observations.

The general conclusion to be drawn from these observations is that water is essential for humans, and human populations are concentrated in regions where they have access to the life-giving liquid.

Activity 2.2 Understanding text: the scientific method

An effective way to check and reinforce your understanding of a key concept in the text is to write down a definition or summary of that concept. This activity requires you to do this for 'scientific method'. Remember that detailed notes are in the Study File. ◄

2.3 How much water do we use?

All the information that we have considered so far, such as that presented in the maps in Figure 2.3, has been *qualitative*. This means that it did not involve numerical information about the number of people in a certain area, or the number of centimetres of rain per year. In this section we shall look at *quantitative* information, that is measurements with numbers attached to them.

Global water use has increased over the centuries not only because the world population has increased but also because we now use water in a huge range of additional ways that Bones would never have dreamt of.

◐ What are the ways in which we use water today that Bones would have been unfamiliar with?

○ We use water in manufacturing industries, in electricity generation and for recreational activities (e.g. swimming pools); and we use a lot more water for washing and cleaning (baths and showers, washing machines and dishwashers, flushing lavatories).

Information about how water is used in the UK is displayed in Table 2.1. In the left-hand column of the table we have listed the main ways in which water is used, and beside each we have indicated the amount of water used each day for each person in the UK. Of course, these figures are estimates rather than precisely measured amounts. The water supply companies have no way of keeping track of how the tens of millions of households actually use all of the water that they supply. They base their estimates on surveys of a range of different types of households, carried out over extended periods of time to allow for seasonal variations, and they use the survey results to estimate typical values for the whole population. So it shouldn't be surprising if your use of water doesn't correspond to the pattern shown in Table 2.1 — you are not necessarily a 'typical' water user!

Table 2.1 Estimates of daily uses of water per person in the UK.

Use of water	Volume/litres
Domestic — mains water supply	
flushing lavatory	44
bath and shower	23
washing machine	16
dishwasher	1
outside use (e.g. garden, car washing)	4
miscellaneous (including drinking, cooking, cleaning)	48
Non-domestic — mains water supply	
commercial and industrial use	189
Non-domestic — direct from rivers and underground supplies	
agriculture	7
electricity generation	220
industry	52

You will meet a wide range of tables of information in this course, but they all have a number of features in common. These are explained in Box 2.2, *Reading tables*.

Box 2.2 Reading tables

Tables are a neat and concise way of displaying information, either numerical or descriptive, particularly when the items of information have common features. It is certainly far easier to find information about various uses of water from Table 2.1 than it would have been if the same information had been wrapped up in 100 words or more in a ten-line paragraph! Since tables should be clear and accurate, they are drawn up according to certain conventions. These are illustrated in Figure 2.4 and you should study this carefully now.

When presented with a table it is useful to ask yourself, 'What is this table telling me?' To answer this question you need to be able to read the information given in the table. Let's look at the data in Table 2.1. To discover the estimated amount of water used in washing machines, for example, you look down the first column to find the row that says 'washing machine', and you read across this row to

the number displayed, which is 16. But 16 what? Well, the column heading makes it clear that the number means that 16 litres of water are used in washing machines. The title of the table then tells you that this 16 litres used in washing machines is water use per person per day in the UK.

How much water, on average, does each person in the UK use per day for baths and showers?

23 litres; don't forget to specify litres, since if you just say '23', nobody will know if you mean gallons, pints, or drops!

One word of reassurance about tables of information in this course: you will not be expected to remember the precise details that they contain unless we specifically tell you to do so. A table like Table 2.1 is a convenient source of reference if you need the details, but *you will not be expected to remember* how many litres of water are used for baths and showers, for example.

Table 2.1   Estimates of daily uses of water per person in the UK.

Use of water	Volume/litres
Domestic — mains water supply	
flushing lavatory	44
bath and shower	23
washing machine	16
dishwasher	1
outside use (e.g. garden, car	4

this number is for ease of reference

heading at top of column tells what information is below

this row is water used in baths and showers

title tells you at a glance what the table is about

heading tells you that figures in the column below it are volumes measured in litres

figures in this column are litres (from heading) per person per day in the UK (from title). Note that 'litres' is not repeated after each number

Figure 2.4   How to read information presented in tables.

Question 2.2   To practise reading the information presented in Table 2.1, answer the following questions.

(a) How much water does the average person in the UK use each day in the home for flushing the lavatory?

(b) What does the number 7 in the third row from the bottom of the table mean? ◄

Table 2.1 contains information about a range of different uses of water. The top part of the table is about domestic uses of the mains water supply, and the bottom part is about uses of water outside the home for agriculture, industry, and so on (non-domestic use). Some of the water for non-domestic use is water from the mains supply, and this is used in offices, shops, schools, and industry. However, large amounts of water, particularly cooling water for electricity generating stations and water for spray irrigation of crops, are taken directly from rivers or underground supplies — the third subheading in the table.

Let's have a more detailed look at some of the numbers in Table 2.1, and do some calculations involving the addition, subtraction, multiplication and division of these numbers. You will need to use your calculator for some or all of these. If you haven't used a calculator much before, or if it is some while since you used one, then you should work through Box 2.3, *Using a calculator for arithmetic*, before trying the calculations in Question 2.6. If you feel *very* confident about your ability with a calculator and know how to do arithmetic in the right order, you may want to skim through this box, and go straight to Question 2.6.

Box 2.3 Using a calculator for arithmetic

Scientific calculators, like the one shown in Figure 2.5, come with an instruction booklet, and this is a handy source of reference, since it will describe how to use the various keys on the calculator to do a wide range of calculations. However, to get you used to working with a calculator, we shall provide directions throughout the course on how to do each type of calculation when it first arises. In this box, we shall cover the standard arithmetic operations: addition +, subtraction −, multiplication ×, and division ÷ or /. We'll use some of the data on UK water use from Table 2.1 as the basis for the calculations.

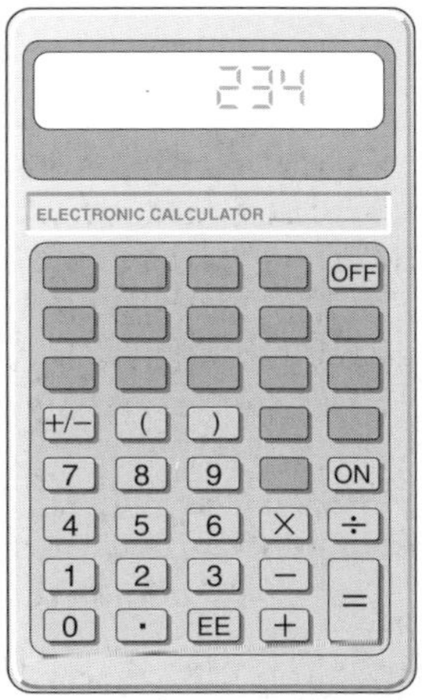

Figure 2.5 A typical scientific calculator. The keys that you will need to use for calculations in this block are shown in blue. We shall explain their use as you come to calculations that require them. Different makes of calculator may have the keys in different positions and the key EE may be labelled EXP or E instead.

Adding numbers with a calculator

Suppose we want to calculate the total use of non-mains water. This means adding the last three numbers in the right-hand column of Table 2.1: 7 + 220 + 52. Let's take this a stage at a time. First, 7 + 220, which you can work out in your head to be 227, and which we can represent by the equation: 7 + 220 = 227. In words, this equation is 'seven plus two hundred and twenty equals two hundred and twenty-seven'. An **equation** like this tells us that whatever is on the left-hand side of the equals (=) sign is exactly equal to whatever is on the right-hand side. So what we are saying in the equation above is that 7 + 220 is exactly the same as 227, or in other words, 7 + 220 is equal to 227.

Now work out this addition with your calculator. To do this you press the keys in the order in which they appear in the equation:

7 then + then 2 2 0 then =

and the answer 227 will appear in the display. Try this procedure for yourself. Of course, the calculator won't tell you that it's 227 *litres* — you have to provide that part of the answer from a knowledge of the meaning of the numbers that you are adding. You added 7 *litres* and 220 *litres*, so the answer must be 227 *litres*. The complete equation can therefore be written as:

7 litres + 220 litres = 227 litres

Now try using your calculator to add some pairs of small numbers that you can also add in your head, and convince yourself that the calculator produces the correct answer. Also try adding some large numbers, and note that the calculator can tackle these as quickly as it does small numbers; there's no need to check the answer by doing the sum on paper!

To add more than two numbers, as required to calculate the total non-domestic, non-mains water use from Table 2.1, you again key in the calculation exactly as it is written. So to work out 7 + 220 + 52, you should key in:

7 then + then 2 2 0 then + then 5 2 then =

and the answer 279 appears in the display, so the answer is 279 litres. The equation for this is:

7 litres + 220 litres + 52 litres = 279 litres

This procedure can be extended to add as many numbers as you wish.

Subtracting numbers with a calculator

If you feel confident with addition, then subtracting with a calculator will be straightforward. You just press the − key instead of the +. Take the water use example from Table 2.1 again: the difference between the use of water for electricity generation and for industry is found by subtracting the appropriate numbers taken from the table, that is, 220 − 52. To work this out with your calculator, you should press the keys in the following order:

2 2 0 then − then 5 2 then =

and the display shows that the answer is 168 (litres). The equation representing this calculation is:

220 litres − 52 litres = 168 litres

You can string together a series of subtractions, in the same way as the series of additions above, and you can mix additions and subtractions in a sequence of operations (which is useful for working out the effect of a series of credits and debits to your bank account).

What the calculator doesn't tell you — the unit of the answer

The calculations that you have just done involved numbers that have a *unit* of measurement associated with them, namely litres (of water per person per day). However, your calculator only deals with the numbers and doesn't deal with the unit. So how do you know what the unit of the answer to a calculation is going to be?

The answer comes from the fact that *the unit must be the same on both sides of an equation*, just as the numbers are. For example, if we want to add 3 litres and 5 litres, then we can write: 3 litres + 5 litres = ... The calculator (or good old-fashioned mental arithmetic) will tell you that 3 + 5 = 8. Then if we want the same unit on both sides of the equation, the answer must be 8 litres, i.e. 3 litres + 5 litres = 8 litres. An important consequence of this requirement for the unit of measurement to be the same on both sides of an equation is that *when we are adding or subtracting quantities, then these quantities must have the same unit*. You can't add 2 litres and 5 gallons; the total amount is neither 7 litres nor 7 gallons. To find the total amount, you need to convert 5 gallons into litres (or 2 litres into gallons) so that you are adding amounts measured in the same unit.

Question 2.3   To practise using your calculator for addition and subtraction, try the following calculations: (a) 46 + 78; (b) 83 + 29; (c) 94 litres + 136 litres; (d) 283 + 729; (e) 56 − 35; (f) 463 metres − 89 metres; (g) 274 grams − 168 grams; (h) 38 + 92 − 61. ◀

Multiplying numbers with a calculator

For multiplication of two numbers, or for multiplying a whole series of numbers, you need to press the calculator keys in the order written for the calculation, just as with addition and subtraction. So if the daily use of water in washing machines is 16 litres, then you find the weekly use by multiplying by 7 (the number of days in a week), that is 16 × 7. So you key in:

1 6 then × then 7 then =

and the answer displayed is 112 (litres per week). If we had wanted to know the amount used in washing machines by a person during their 75-year lifetime, then the appropriate sum would be 16 litres per day × 365 days per year × 75 years. Keying this as:

1 6 × 3 6 5 × 7 5 =

produces the answer 438 000 (litres in a 75-year lifetime).

Note that in this course, and in general in scientific use, numbers are printed with a space between thousands and hundreds, not a comma.

Dividing numbers with a calculator

As with the other three arithmetical operations discussed above, if you can write down a division sum as a series of numbers and symbols, then you can simply key them into the calculator in the order that they are written. For example, if your annual use of water was 54 750 litres, then you can calculate your daily use by dividing this by 365, so the calculation is 54 750 ÷ 365, (or $\frac{54\,750}{365}$ which is often written as 54 750/365). To do this on the calculator, you need to press the keys as follows:

5 4 7 5 0 ÷ 3 6 5 =

and the answer is 150. So your use of water would be 150 litres per day.

Question 2.4   To practise using your calculator for multiplication and division, try the following calculations: (a) 48 × 21; (b) 95 × 24; (c) 761 × 13; (d) 293 litres × 212; (e) 94 ÷ 47; (f) 392 ÷ 49; (g) 378 metres ÷ 54; (h) 24 × 32 ÷ 8; (i) 245 × 76 ÷ 20. ◀

Doing arithmetic in the right order

Many calculations in science involve a series of operations — additions, subtractions, multiplications and divisions — and to get the correct answer these operations must be carried out in the correct order. Consider the following examples.

Suppose two people each have two bottles of water, and they then buy a box of 6 bottles to share. You can see from Figure 2.6a that they have a total of ten bottles — that is, two lots of two plus another six. We can write this as a mathematical equation: $2 \times 2 + 6 = 10$. Try this on your calculator, ② ✕ ② ➕ ⑥ ＝, and check that it gives the answer 10.

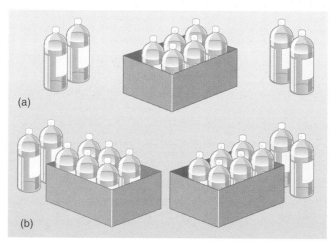

(a)

(b)

Figure 2.6 Two different sets of bottles.

Now suppose the couple initially had the box of six bottles, and then each bought two more bottles; the total number of bottles would be: $6 + 2 \times 2$. If you work this out with your calculator, ⑥ ➕ ② ✕ ② ＝, then you will again get the answer 10. So the calculator doesn't distinguish between $2 \times 2 + 6$ and $6 + 2 \times 2$. This is because the calculator uses the same rule that mathematicians and scientists use when faced with calculations like these,* namely

carry out multiplying before adding

If you ignore this rule, and do the calculation $6 + 2 \times 2$ in your head in the order in which it is printed, then you find that $6 + 2 = 8$, and $8 \times 2 = 16$. This is clearly the wrong answer to this calculation — the couple must have ten bottles, just as they had in the first example! The reason that you get the wrong answer in the second case is that you have worked out 'six plus two', and then multiplied by two which means that the calculation

*A warning here! Some older scientific calculators may not have these rules built into them, so check your calculator now by using it to do the two calculations.

assumes (incorrectly) that the couple have two boxes of six bottles as well as two lots of two bottles.

Now consider a different situation. Suppose that these two people each buy a box of 6 bottles of water to take home and each also buy 2 separate bottles. There is a total of 16 bottles, as you can see in Figure 2.6b. How do we write down the calculation for the total number of bottles this time? Since each person has $6 + 2$ bottles, and there are two people, your first guess might be $6 + 2 \times 2$. But if you do this calculation using the 'multiplication before addition' rule — as your calculator would — then you will get the answer 10. (This is exactly the same as one of the calculations that you worked out earlier.) However, if you ignore the rule and work out the calculation in your head in the order in which it is written, then $6 + 2 = 8$, and $8 \times 2 = 16$, which is the correct number of bottles in this case. So to get the correct answer, we need to do the addition *first* in this calculation, and so we need a way to indicate that the addition must be carried out first.

When we want to over-ride the standard rule of 'multiplication before addition', we put brackets around the part of the calculation that must be done first. So the calculation for Figure 2.6b would be written as $(6 + 2) \times 2$ or, alternatively, as $2 \times (6 + 2)$. *Brackets mean 'do this first'*, so, in this calculation, you (or your calculator) must first work out the contents of the brackets, and then do the multiplication.

You can do calculations with brackets in them on a scientific calculator by making use of its brackets keys, ⦅ and ⦆. Try this with your calculator — to work out $(6 + 2) \times 2$ you simply key in the calculation as it is written:

⦅ ⑥ ➕ ② ⦆ ✕ ② ＝

and the answer 16 will be displayed. The calculator works out the contents of the brackets before doing the multiplication.

Strictly speaking, brackets are only needed to over-ride the 'multiplication before addition' rule, and they are not needed in the calculations $(2 \times 2) + 6$ or $6 + (2 \times 2)$. In the absence of the brackets, you or your calculator would follow the rule and do the multiplication first, before the addition. However, brackets are often used in calculations for clarity, even where they are not strictly necessary. For example, the calculation $6 \times 4 + 12 \times 5$ is more understandable and 'readable' if it is printed as

$(6 \times 4) + (12 \times 5)$. The brackets are not essential here, because the rules indicate that you (or your calculator) must do the two multiplications first anyway.

The calculation $6 \times (4 + 12) \times 5$ is quite different. Here the brackets tell you to work out $4 + 12$ first, before doing the multiplications. The answer you get (480) is quite different from $6 \times 4 + 12 \times 5$ (which equals 84), so the brackets are essential in this calculation. Check this for yourself by keying in the two calculations, the first one with brackets and the second one without brackets.

In this course we shall use brackets that are not essential, wherever they make calculations look clearer, and you will be encouraged to take the same approach in your responses to questions that involve calculations.

So far we have considered the mathematical rules involving $\times$, $+$ and brackets in arithmetic. What about situations where $-$ and $\div$ are involved? The rules then are:

first (...) , then $\div$ and $\times$, then $+$ and $-$

There is one final point to make about the order in which you do arithmetic. When faced with a calculation that includes a series of multiplications and divisions (or a series of additions and subtractions), then you work through the calculation *from left to right in the order in which it is written*. To understand the importance of this, compare the following two ways of working out a simple calculation:

correct way, left to right: $16 \div 2 \times 4 = 8 \times 4 = 32$

wrong way, not left to right: $16 \div 2 \times 4 = 16 \div 8 = 2$

The correct calculation could have been expressed more clearly as $(16 \div 2) \times 4$, though the brackets are not strictly necessary. If the calculation that we intended to do was the second of the two shown above, then we would need to write it as $16 \div (2 \times 4)$.

There is an easy way to remember the correct order in which operations should be carried out. The rules are neatly summed up in the word: **BODMAS**.

B stands for **B**rackets
O stands for **o**ver
D stands for **D**ivide
M stands for **M**ultiply
A stands for **A**dd
S stands for **S**ubtract

The order of letters in BODMAS tells you the order in which you must carry out the operations. The first two letters indicate that **B**rackets have precedence **o**ver all the other operations; in other words you must work out the operation that is inside the brackets before you carry out any of the other operations. You then do the **D**ivisions and **M**ultiplications, and finally the **A**dditions and **S**ubtractions. You must also remember that in any part of the calculation that involves just divisions and multiplications, or just additions and subtractions, you must work from left to right, i.e. in the order in which the calculation is written.

(Note that BODMAS is a mnemonic (pronounced 'nem-on-ick'), which is a set of letters that make up some memorable word or name that helps you remember the correct order of a sequence of things. For example, the name ROY G BIV is a mnemonic that tells you the order of the colours in the rainbow: red, orange, yellow, green, blue, indigo and violet.)

Question 2.5   To practise the BODMAS rules, try the following calculations in your head and with your calculator: (a) $26 - 12 + 4$; (b) $16 + 12 \times 2$; (c) $(16 + 12) \times 2$; (d) $35 - 7 \times 2$; (e) $(35 - 7) \times 2$; (f) $180 \div 10 \times 3$; (g) $180 \div (10 \times 3)$; (h) $(10 + 5) \times (3 + 1)$. ◀

The reliability of calculators

Unfortunately it is possible to get the wrong answer when using a calculator. This is not an indication of the unreliability of modern electronic technology; it's an indication that a calculator is only as good as the fingers that press the keys! It is easy to press the wrong key, or to press keys in the wrong order, and hence to end up with a meaningless answer. It is good practice to check the numbers that appear in the display as you key them in, and to repeat a calculation if the answer seems suspicious.

Of course that then begs the question of how you know if the answer looks suspicious. There are simple things to look out for: when adding numbers, the answer has to be bigger than the largest of the numbers you are adding, and when subtracting two numbers the answer must be smaller than the larger of the two numbers. When you multiply two numbers larger than 1, the result must be larger than either of the numbers, and dividing one number by another that is larger than 1 always produces a number that is less than the first number.

It is also good practice to estimate an answer using simpler numbers. For example, you can estimate the answer to 96 ÷ 47 by working out (in your head) 100 ÷ 50, and using the answer 2 as a guide.

Practising using your calculator

There will be many opportunities for you to use your calculator during this course, and it is important that you are able to do calculations reliably and efficiently. The basic +, −, × and ÷ operations that have been introduced in this box and the order in which you carry out these operations are at the core of most calculations, so it's important that you feel confident about doing them.

Question 2.6   Check that you can use your calculator for arithmetic by using the information in Table 2.1, to calculate:

(a) the total domestic use, the total non-domestic use and the overall total use of water per person per day in the UK;

(b) from your answer to (a), the difference between the non-domestic and the domestic uses;

(c) the volume of water used per person *per week*, and per person *per year*, for baths and showers;

(d) how many days' water for flushing domestic lavatories could be provided by the water used in one day for electricity generation? ◄

Question 2.7   Write down an arithmetical expression (for example, (20 × 4) − 10) for each of the following situations, and use your calculator to work out the answers.

(a) If the daily domestic use of water by a particular family of four is typically 440 litres, what is the annual use per person?

(b) Three people sharing accommodation each use 150 litres of water in a day. They use 15 litres, 25 litres and 40 litres, respectively, for baths or showers. How much water do they together use for all other purposes?

(c) What is the estimated daily volume of water used for flushing lavatories, baths and showers, and in washing machines by a family of four 'typical' people? ◄

The information in Table 2.1 doesn't tell the whole story about water use in the UK. The table only includes water supplied by water mains and water taken from rivers and from underground supplies. However, the dominant source of water for agriculture in the UK — for growing crops — is direct precipitation of rain and snow. Also power stations and industries that use large amounts of water are often sited on the coast or on river estuaries, and use seawater for cooling purposes; water from these sources is not included in Table 2.1. Cooling water is generally returned to its source — river, estuary or sea — albeit a few degrees warmer. The water returned to a river from a power station may well be removed again further downstream to be used for industry, agriculture or domestic consumption.

Activity 2.1   Monitoring your study (continued)

Have you recorded your study times on the grid in the Study File? If not, spend a few minutes now completing the grid for your study of Section 2 so far. ◄

2.4 Saving water

In the previous section we considered the daily water use per person in the UK. The figures for domestic use that were given in Table 2.1 are estimates for the whole population, averaged over the year. Clearly there will be seasonal variations in domestic water use, and when droughts lead to water shortages there can be dramatic changes to the levels and patterns of water use. In this section we shall look at some of the savings that could be made in water consumption to cope with drought conditions (or to reduce water bills that are based on the amount of water supplied). In doing this we shall make use of ideas about fractions, ratios and percentages, which are all useful ways of comparing numbers. So before we look at various savings in water consumption, study Box 2.4, *Fractions, ratios and percentages*.

Box 2.4 Fractions, ratios and percentages

Fractions, ratios and percentages are all ways of expressing proportions, that is they show the relationship between two or more numbers.

Fractions

The term **fraction** means that a quantity is part of a whole, and is the result of dividing a whole amount into a number of equal parts. So if you say that you can eat one quarter of a pie, written as $\frac{1}{4}$, then you are dividing the pie into four equal parts and saying that you can eat one of those parts. After you take your $\frac{1}{4}$ of the pie, three of the four quarters will remain, so the fraction remaining is three-quarters or $\frac{3}{4}$. The numbers $\frac{1}{4}$ and $\frac{3}{4}$ are examples of fractions.

Fractions can be written in two different ways: three-quarters can be written as $\frac{3}{4}$ or 3/4. Both forms will be used in this course. The first is used when writing out a calculation, but the second way is sometimes more convenient in a line of text.

Any fraction can be expressed in a variety of equivalent forms. Thus two-quarters of a fruit pie, 2/4, means two of the four equal parts, and you know that this is the same amount as one half, 1/2. So 2/4 and 1/2 are said to be **equivalent fractions** because they are of equal value. Figure 2.7 shows four rectangular blocks of chocolate, of identical sizes, but divided into different numbers of equal-sized pieces. The darker areas can be expressed as different fractions, but all of the darker areas are the same size, so the four fractions are all equivalent. This means that:

$$\frac{3}{8} = \frac{6}{16} = \frac{9}{24} = \frac{15}{40}$$

In words, we would say 'three-eighths equals six-sixteenths equals nine-twenty-fourths equals fifteen-fortieths'. Or an alternative way of saying this would be 'three over eight equals six over sixteen equals nine over twenty-four equals fifteen over forty'.

Note that you can change 3/8 to the equivalent fraction 6/16 by multiplying both the number on the top and the number on the bottom by 2. Similarly, you can convert 3/8 to 9/24 by multiplying both the top and the bottom by 3.

● By what number do you have to multiply both the top and the bottom of the fraction 3/8 to end up with 15/40?

○ 5, because $5 \times 3 = 15$, and $5 \times 8 = 40$.

If you take any fraction, and multiply *both* the number on the top of the fraction and the number on the bottom by the same number — any one you care to choose — you will produce an equivalent fraction. Thus:

$$\frac{1}{3} = \frac{2}{6} = \frac{4}{12} = \frac{20}{60} = \frac{200}{600}$$

Here we have multiplied the top and the bottom of the fraction $\frac{1}{3}$ in turn by 2 (to get $\frac{2}{6}$), then by another 2, then by 5, and finally by 10.

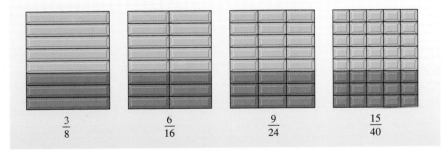

$$\frac{3}{8} \qquad \frac{6}{16} \qquad \frac{9}{24} \qquad \frac{15}{40}$$

Figure 2.7 Equivalent fractions of chocolate bars. The darker areas are all the same size.

Fractions are usually expressed with the smallest possible whole numbers on the top and the bottom. Working out the equivalent fraction with these smallest numbers is really a matter of finding numbers that can be divided into *both* the number on the top of the fraction *and* the number on the bottom. For example,

$$\frac{60}{300} = \frac{6}{30} = \frac{3}{15} = \frac{1}{5}$$

so these are all equivalent fractions.

Here we first divided the numbers on the top and the bottom of the first fraction by 10 to get $\frac{6}{30}$, then we divided both numbers by 2 to get $\frac{3}{15}$, and finally by 3 to end up with $\frac{1}{5}$.

Note that all four of these fractions are equivalent, but we would normally use the fraction with the lowest numbers, $\frac{1}{5}$.

Working out an equivalent fraction with the smallest whole numbers can be done step by step, as in the example above. It's best to start by seeing if you can divide by simple numbers, like 10, 2, 5. Thus if the numbers on the top and the bottom of a fraction both end in zero, then you can divide them both by 10 (first step in the example above). If they are both even numbers, then you can divide them by 2 (second step above). If both end in either a five or a zero, then they can be divided by five.

So to express $\frac{10}{40}$ with the smallest whole numbers, you would divide the top and the bottom by 10. This division can be illustrated by 'cancelling out' the zeros by crossing them through with a diagonal line:

$$\frac{1\cancel{0}}{4\cancel{0}} = \frac{1}{4}$$

This cancelling process is the same as dividing — in this case dividing

by 10. If there are more zeros, then more cancelling is possible. Thus:

$$\frac{300}{2\,000} = \frac{3\cancel{00}}{2\,0\cancel{00}} = \frac{3}{20}$$

⬤ How would the following fractions normally be expressed?

$$\frac{450}{1050}; \frac{420}{660}$$

○ $$\frac{450}{1050} = \frac{45}{105} = \frac{9}{21} = \frac{3}{7},$$

and $$\frac{420}{660} = \frac{42}{66} = \frac{21}{33} = \frac{7}{11}.$$

In the first case we have divided in turn by 10, by 5 and by 3; in the second case we have divided by 10, then 2, and then 3.

Now it isn't just numbers that we can divide by, or cancel, in fractions. We can often do the same with the units. Suppose we want to know what fraction of domestic water use in the UK is for washing machines; then using information from Table 2.1 and the answer to Question 2.6a, we have to divide 16 litres by 136 litres. So

$$\frac{16\,\cancel{\text{litres}}}{136\,\cancel{\text{litres}}} = \frac{16}{136} = \frac{8}{68} = \frac{4}{34} = \frac{2}{17}$$

So $\frac{2}{17}$ domestic water use is for washing machines. Notice that in the first step above we cancelled the unit of litres, since this was the same on the top and the bottom of the fraction.

This cancellation of units explains the convention that we use for headings in tables. If you look back to Table 2.1, you'll see that the second column is headed 'Volume/litres'. Now the volume of water used for flushing lavatories is 44 litres, so in this case:

volume/litres = 44 litres/litres

$$= \frac{44\,\cancel{\text{litres}}}{\cancel{\text{litres}}} = 44$$

since the litres cancel out from the top and the bottom. So if we take the volume in litres and divide it by litres then we end up with a simple number, and that is the number that is entered in the table. The table heading 'Volume/litres' reminds us that we have cancelled out the unit to get the simple numbers in the table, and conversely that we need to re-attach the unit in the heading to the number when we extract it from the table.

Until now we have only considered fractions for which the number on the top is smaller than the number on the bottom, so these fractions are part of a whole. However, it is possible to have a fraction in which the number on the top is *larger* than the number on the bottom, such as $\frac{5}{4}$ or $\frac{13}{8}$, and these are sometimes called 'improper fractions'. The fraction $\frac{5}{4}$ simply means five quarters (of a pie, or whatever); only four quarters can come from a whole pie, so the fifth quarter must come from another pie.

Ratios

Looking again at the chocolate bars in Figure 2.7, you can see that 3 out of 8 pieces are darkened in the first, 6 out of 16 in the second, 9 out of 24 in the third and 15 out of 40 in the fourth. These pairs of numbers, which form equivalent fractions, are said to be in the same **ratio**. So any pairs of numbers that form equivalent fractions are in the same ratio.

⬤ Which of the following pairs of numbers are in the same ratio as (6, 20)? (3, 10), (12, 40), (12, 30), (30, 100), (24, 100)

➡

6/20 = 3/10 = 12/40 = 30/100, so these are all equivalent fractions, and therefore the pairs of numbers from which they are formed are in the same ratio. Using the lowest whole numbers, we say that these pairs of numbers are all in the ratio 3 to 10. The fractions 12/30 (= 6/15) and 24/100 (= 6/25) are *not* equivalent to 6/20, so (12, 30) and (24, 100) are *not* in the same ratio as (6, 20).

Ratios are often written as two numbers separated by a colon (:). So a fraction such as 3/10 is equivalent to a ratio of 3 to 10 and this is often written as 3 : 10.

You need to take care when asked to give the ratio of two numbers, as the following example shows.

Suppose 2 out of 10 people in the UK drink bottled water. What is the ratio of people who drink bottled water to those that don't?

The ratio is 2 : 8.

Did you fall into the trap and answer 2 : 10? This is the ratio of people who drink bottled water to the *total* number of people. Of course if we'd asked what is the ratio of people who don't drink bottled water to those who do, the answer would have been 8 : 2. So always read the question carefully!

Ratios are particularly useful where the relative proportions of two or more parts of a whole are being considered. For example, the ratio of males to females in the general population of the UK is about 1 : 1. One last point about ratios that is very important is that ratios do not have units attached to them.

Percentages

You have probably met percentages in various contexts, such as a 3% pay rise, 10% interest on a loan, or 20% off goods in a sale. A **percentage** is a fraction expressed in hundredths. So 1/2 — one-half — is 50/100, or fifty-hundredths, and we say that this is 50 per cent, which is usually written as 50%. This literally means 50 in every 100. The advantage of using percentages is that we are always talking about hundredths, so percentages are easy to compare, whereas with fractions we can divide the whole thing into arbitrary numbers of parts, eighths, sixteenths, fiftieths, or whatever we choose. It is not immediately obvious that 19/25 is larger than 15/20, but if these fractions are expressed as percentages — 76% and 75%, respectively — then it is easy to see that the former number is the larger of the two. But how do we convert fractions to percentages, or percentages to fractions?

The way that you convert a fraction into a percentage is by *multiplying* the fraction by 100%. So to convert 1/2 to a percentage:

$$\frac{1}{2} \times 100\% = \frac{1 \times 100\%}{2} = 50\%$$

Three-quarters, 3/4, converts to:

$$\frac{3}{4} \times 100\% = \frac{3 \times 100\%}{4} = 75\%$$

To work $\frac{3}{4} \times 100\%$ out with a calculator, you would key in:

$\boxed{3} \; \boxed{\div} \; \boxed{4} \; \boxed{\times} \; \boxed{1}\boxed{0}\boxed{0} \; \boxed{=}$

or alternatively to work out

$\frac{3 \times 100\%}{4}$, you would key in:

$\boxed{3} \; \boxed{\times} \; \boxed{1}\boxed{0}\boxed{0} \; \boxed{\div} \; \boxed{4} \; \boxed{=}$

and the answer appears as 75 (%).

On occasions you will need to convert a percentage to a fraction, and to do this you have to *divide* by 100. In other words, you carry out the reverse procedure to the one you used to convert a fraction to a percentage.

Thus $75\% = \frac{75}{100} = \frac{15}{20} = \frac{3}{4}$

(having divided the top and the bottom of the fraction by 5, then by 5 again),

and $15\% = \frac{15}{100} = \frac{3}{20}$

(having divided the top and the bottom by 5).

Calculating fractions and percentages of numbers

Finally, let's consider how you would work out what $\frac{3}{4}$, or 75%, of 36 is. First think about what $\frac{3}{4}$ of 36 means. It means divide 36 into 4 equal parts or quarters (36 ÷ 4 = 9). Then, since we want three-quarters, which is three times as big, we multiply one of these parts by three (9 × 3 = 27). So $\frac{3}{4}$ of 36 is 27. We can write this calculation as $\frac{3}{4} \times 36$, because this means the same thing as

$$3 \times \frac{36}{4}, \text{ or } \frac{3 \times 36}{4}.$$

So '$\frac{3}{4}$ of' a number means multiply that number by $\frac{3}{4}$.

What is $\frac{2}{3}$ of 18?

$$\frac{2}{3} \times 18 = \frac{2 \times 18}{3} = \frac{2 \times 6}{1} = 12$$

Working out 75% of a number can be done in a similar way if you remember that $75\% = \frac{75}{100}$. So 75% of 40 is:

$$\frac{75}{100} \times 40 = 30$$

In summary, you can see that fractions, ratios and percentages are all ways of expressing a proportion. So, for example, if you eat $\frac{1}{4}$ of a pie, the ratio of the amount you eat to the total pie is $1:4$, and the percentage that you eat is 25%.

Question 2.8 Convert the following fractions to percentages (using your calculator if you wish):

(a) $\frac{7}{10}$; (b) $\frac{9}{20}$; (c) $\frac{13}{25}$; (d) $\frac{63}{100}$; (e) $\frac{140}{200}$; (f) $\frac{30}{20}$. ◀

Question 2.9 Convert the following percentages to fractions with the smallest possible whole numbers on the top and the bottom:

(a) 60%; (b) 64%; (c) 65%; (d) 67%. ◀

Question 2.10 Work out:

(a) $\frac{2}{5}$ of 20; (b) $\frac{7}{8}$ of 24;

(c) 15% of £60; (d) 60% of 5 metres. ◀

Let's return to the question of how water consumption could be reduced in a drought.

⬤ For which of the categories of domestic water use shown in Table 2.1 would your household be likely to reduce its water consumption in a serious drought?

◯ Only you know the answer to this question — it is obviously very subjective! However, if you have a garden, savings in outside use may have been top of your list (use of hosepipes and sprinklers is often the first thing to be prohibited in a drought). You may also have considered savings in water use for baths and showers (in a recent drought, it was suggested that people should share a bath or shower with a partner) or for flushing the lavatory (putting a brick or bottle in the cistern is recommended as a way of reducing the volume of water used per flush).

To illustrate the savings that might be made, we shall consider the strategy adopted by a hypothetical household, the Browns. They agree to reduce their normal pattern of water use, shown in Table 2.2, by:

• not using any water outside

• reducing water use for baths and showers to 2/3 of normal

• putting a 1-litre bottle in their 10-litre flush cistern.

The savings that the Browns make by adopting this three-point strategy are explored in the questions that follow. In answering these questions, you will need to express the Browns' savings as fractions, ratios and percentages, and then construct a table in order to decide which of these forms makes it easiest to compare the savings made.

Table 2.2 Average daily water use by the Brown household.

Use of water	Volume/litres
flushing lavatory	120
bath and shower	96
washing machine	54
dishwasher	24
outside use (e.g. garden, car washing)	20
miscellaneous (including drinking, cooking, cleaning)	86

Question 2.11 (a) What is the daily saving in the Browns' water consumption if they don't use any water outside? Express your answer as a fraction, as a ratio and as a percentage of the present total daily water use. *Don't forget to cancel units where appropriate!*

(b) What saving would result from their strategy to reduce their water use for baths and showers to 2/3 of the normal use? Express your answer in litres, and as a fraction, as a ratio and as a percentage of their present total daily water use.

(c) Now consider the savings from their third strategy. What fraction of their normal use for flushing the lavatory will be saved, and what is this saving as a percentage of the normal use?

(d) What total daily saving results from their strategy of reducing their water use for flushing the lavatory? Express your answer in litres, and as a fraction, as a ratio and as a percentage of the present total daily water use. ◀

Question 2.12   Fill in Table 2.3 with the answers from Question 2.11. Which of the three ways used to express the savings makes them easiest to compare? ◀

Table 2.3   Water savings of the Browns.

Use of water	Fraction	Ratio	Percentage
outside use			
bath/shower			
flushing lavatory			

Question 2.13   The Browns' neighbours, the Patels, manage to make daily savings of 70 litres on their normal use of 500 litres. By comparing the percentage savings of the Browns and the Patels, decide which household makes the greater economies. (*Hint*   You will first need to work out the Brown's total daily savings.) ◀

The answers to Questions 2.12 and 2.13 should have convinced you that percentages are much more convenient than either fractions or ratios for comparing each of the savings that the Browns made, and for comparing the savings made by the Browns with the savings made by the Patels.

2.5   Water for life

You calculated earlier (Question 2.6) that 604 litres of water are used each day in the UK for each person in the population. That's a lot of water! Also, even though the *domestic* usage of 136 litres per person per day is only about 23% of that 604 litres figure, the domestic use is still a large amount. Life in the developed world has come to depend on such plentiful supplies of water being available at the turn of a tap. In Section 2.4 you calculated some reductions in water use that might be made in drought conditions in the UK, but these were relatively small changes. Just imagine how your lifestyle and your use of water would change if every day you had to carry 136 litres of water, weighing 136 kilograms, from a well or a tap that was 100 metres away from your house! Your water use would undoubtedly decrease to an amount that was much closer to the few litres a day that are really essential to maintain life — just a small fraction of the 136 litres currently used.

The ultimate test of how essential water is for life comes when people are deprived of water. Survival times without water depend critically on the prevailing conditions; somebody who is stranded in the hot sun of the Sahara Desert would not survive for nearly as long as a person shut in a cool dark cellar. Possibly the record for survival without water is for a young Austrian man, who in 1979 was put into a holding cell and then forgotten by the police. He was discovered 18 days later, close to death. However, it is unusual for a person to survive for more than 7–10 days without water, and the survival time would be far shorter in a hot desert.

The reasons that we are so dependent on water are readily apparent if you think about the range of different water-based fluids in the body and the essential roles that they fulfil.

⬤ What fluids can you think of that are found in, or on, the human body?

◯ You may have thought of blood, urine, sweat, tears, saliva, digestive juices, and mucous fluid in the nose and lungs.

A wide range of our essential bodily functions depend on these water-based fluids. It is fortunate, therefore, that in normal circumstances our bodies have a remarkable ability to regulate their fluid levels so that all of these functions continue to operate efficiently. So, for example, when the water content of your body is too low then you feel thirsty and will find something to drink, and when you drink large volumes of liquid (not necessarily pure water!) your body will increase production of urine to remove the excess liquid. However, when the body is deprived of water, the many functions that depend on water-based fluids are disrupted, and the consequences become increasingly severe as water deprivation increases.

Plants also contain large amounts of water-based fluids, as we shall discuss in more detail later in this block, and they too need regular supplies of water for their growth. The desert region where our friend Bones was discovered is now inhospitable to humans, not only because of the lack of water for drinking, but also because water is not available for growing food. However, though humans cannot live in the desert without bringing in water supplies, there are organisms that can exist on the meagre amounts of water that are naturally available in these regions, and we shall discuss how they manage this later in this book.

2.6 Summary of Section 2

Each main section of the book ends with a summary of important points and skills in that section. These are the points that you should know and remember, and the skills that you should be familiar with.

Humans and other organisms need water to live; human populations are therefore low in desert areas where there is a lack of water.

The scientific method describes the way that scientific knowledge and understanding develop by revising or replacing existing hypotheses in response to new observations and discoveries.

Illustrations in the text can be used to convey important information, and should be 'read' carefully.

Tables are a clear, concise way to display information. A table should have a title, and should have column headings that include information about the units of all measured quantities.

Calculators are a useful tool for addition, subtraction, multiplication and division.

BODMAS is a mnemonic for remembering the order of carrying out mathematical operations in a calculation: *B*rackets *o*ver *D*ivide and *M*ultiply, then *A*dd and *S*ubtract. Also, for any part of a calculation that involves just divisions and multiplications, or just additions and subtractions, you must work from left to right.

Fractions, ratios and percentages are convenient ways of comparing relative amounts of two quantities. It is easier to compare two proportions expressed as percentages rather than as fractions or ratios.

Activity 2.1   Monitoring your study (continued)

Now that you have completed Section 2, you should review your log of study times in the Study File and should consider the questions that are posed there. ◀

Activity 2.3   Finding time and motivation for study

In order to help you think about your study pattern for Section 3, study the video 'Finding time and motivation for study' which eavesdrops on a group of students discussing when they study, for how long they study at a session, how they fit study into a busy schedule, and how they motivate themselves to study. ◀

Water in living organisms

One thing that all living organisms have in common is that they contain water. This may not be obvious, because the fluids that are obtained from animals and plants are not pure water. Blood, urine and sweat from animals, and the sap from plants all contain a variety of substances, and they look, taste and smell quite different from water. However, many experiments on these fluids, and on those from a huge range of other organisms, have demonstrated that water is the major component present in every case.

In this section we shall investigate *how much* water is present in living organisms. We start by discussing how water content is measured, and then you will be able to do the first practical work for the course — an experiment to measure the water content of a potato. This will provide an interesting, and perhaps surprising, result which can be compared with data on the water content of a variety of plants and animals, including humans. The water content of humans and potatoes are not much different from the water content of camels and cacti, even though these latter organisms can survive in hot, dry desert conditions. At the end of this section we shall discuss how camels and cacti manage to survive in conditions that are so inhospitable from the human viewpoint.

Interwoven with our theme of 'water in living organisms' is the development of a variety of skills. The experiment will introduce skills associated with practical work in science, including planning, measuring, recording and analysing data, and critically evaluating what you have done. Using these skills is part of scientific inquiry. We shall also be developing science skills associated with units of measurement and the maths skills of using decimals and of reading information from graphs. You will continue the work on planning your study that you started in Section 2. However, we begin by looking at the skill of identifying key points.

Active reading: identifying key points

Reading can be a passive process, but it can also be an active one. The questions and activities that are built into this block are designed to encourage you to think about the text as you study. Answering the questions and doing the activities in Section 2 should have convinced you that *doing* something associated with the text is far more effective than just reading it.

It is important to realize that the course books are *work*books rather than textbooks, and you should feel free to write and draw in them as you study. As you read, you should try to identify the key points in the text. You may like to use a highlighting (fluorescent) pen to pick out words and phrases that correspond to main ideas or key points, i.e. those phrases that carry the crucial explanation of a point or a definition of something. Alternatively you may prefer to underline the important words and phrases. In addition, you will find that constantly asking yourself 'what are the key points?' will help you get to grips with the content of the text. The highlighted words and phrases will also be useful for summarizing and revising.

What you choose to highlight (or underline), and how much, rather depends on you. At first you might be tempted to highlight the majority of the text, but try to *be selective*, and *just highlight the key points*. We have provided an example to help you with this technique in Activity 3.5.

Activity 3.1   *Planning your study*

In addition to the study components that you used in Section 2 — this book, the Study File, and a video — there is some practical work to carry out in this section. Try to plan now the day and time you will carry out the practical work, using the advice and grid provided in the Study File. Remember to keep a log of the time actually spent studying Section 3, for which you can use the same grid. ◀

3.1   Water — the vital ingredient

The presence of water in all known living organisms has led scientists to accept the hypothesis that every living thing contains water. Remember, though, that a hypothesis is an explanation provisionally adopted to account for certain observations. The hypothesis that all living things contain water is consistent with all of the many experiments and observations that have been carried out. But if anybody were to discover a form of life that did not contain water, whether on Earth or on some other planet, then this hypothesis would have to be abandoned. However, until that happens we shall assume that the hypothesis is correct, and we shall now look more closely at the *amount* of water in living things.

It is not easy to measure the amount of water in a *living* organism (or in part of the organism), but it is straightforward to do it immediately after the organism has died or, in the case of plants, been harvested. In the case of plants that are gathered for food, water contents have been measured to provide dietary information. The amount of water in cabbage, for example, has been determined by weighing raw cabbage leaves, drying them to remove all of the water that they contain, and then weighing them again.

● Suppose that 800 grams of cabbage leaves are slowly dried in an oven, and then found to weigh only 100 grams. How much water did the leaves contain?

○ The amount of water is the difference between the initial 800 grams and the final 100 grams, assuming that only water is released when the leaves are dried. So there were 700 grams of water in the cabbage leaves.

Notice the assumption that has been made here: we are assuming that only water is released in the drying process. This is not strictly true, since small amounts of other substances will also be released, but it is a good enough approximation for present purposes. Scientists are often willing to make simplifying assumptions, and this is acceptable as long as these assumptions are clearly stated.

The number 700 in the answer above is accompanied by the appropriate unit, grams. Units are essential information about any measured quantity, and here, as in the rest of this course and in science generally, we have used the metric unit of mass. Box 3.1, *Units of measurement*, reviews the basic metric units of mass, length and time, which you will meet over and over again as you study science.

Box 3.1 Units of measurement

If you were told that the length of a piece of string was 37, you would be rather baffled. 37 what? Is it 37 metres, 37 centimetres, 37 feet, or even 37 miles? Similarly, if somebody says that an adult male friend weighs 100, what does this mean? These examples highlight the importance of having defined units with which to make measurements and the importance of quoting the units when you want to communicate what you have measured.

OUR CAT WEIGHS 4 .

In science the units used are known as **SI units**, which is an abbreviation for 'Système Internationale d'Unités' (International System of Units). In 1960 an international conference formally approved this set of metric units as standard, so replacing the many different national systems of measurement that had been used in science up to that time. The advantage of having a standard set of units is that everyone uses them, and there is no need to convert laboriously from one system to another to compare results in different countries. So although in everyday life in the UK at the end of the 20th century people may still buy milk and beer in pints, and measure distances between towns in miles, in the scientific community SI units are used almost exclusively.

So what are these units? At this stage we shall just introduce the SI units of length, time and mass; other units will be introduced later in the course.

The basic SI unit of length is the **metre**, which is abbreviated to **m**

The basic SI unit of time is the **second**, which is abbreviated to **s**

The basic SI unit of mass is the **kilogram**, which is abbreviated to **kg**

Although a metre is a conveniently sized unit for measuring the height of a person or the width of a room, it is the wrong sort of size to use for quoting the distance between London and Edinburgh, or the breadth of a pinhead. It is therefore conventional and convenient to use larger and smaller multiples of the metre when appropriate — *note that these are also SI units*. So, for example, large distances can be measured in kilometres (km), and small distances or lengths can be measured in millimetres (mm). The prefix **kilo** means 'one thousand', so a kilometre is one thousand metres. The prefix **milli** means 'one-thousandth', so a millimetre is one-thousandth of a metre. Put another way one metre is one thousand millimetres. Therefore $1 \text{ km} = 1\,000 \text{ m}$, $1 \text{ mm} = \frac{1}{1\,000} \text{ m}$ and $1 \text{ m} = 1\,000 \text{ mm}$.

● How many millimetres are there in 1 kilometre?

○ $1 \text{ km} = 1\,000 \text{ m}$ and $1 \text{ m} = 1\,000 \text{ mm}$, so $1 \text{ km} = 1\,000 \times 1\,000 \text{ mm} = 1\,000\,000 \text{ mm}$.

Another common prefix that you may have met is **centi** (as in centimetre, abbreviated to cm), which means 'one-hundredth'. So $1 \text{ cm} = \frac{1}{100} \text{ m}$, and this means that $100 \text{ cm} = 100 \times \frac{1}{100} \text{ m} = \frac{100}{100} \text{ m} = 1 \text{ m}$, that is $1 \text{ m} = 100 \text{ cm}$.

● How many centimetres are there in 25 metres?

○ Since $1 \text{ m} = 100 \text{ cm}$, $25 \text{ m} = 25 \times 100 \text{ cm} = 2\,500 \text{ cm}$.

If you didn't know how many millimetres there were in a centimetre, you could use their definitions to work this out. From the definitions,

$$1 \text{ m} = 100 \text{ cm} = 1\,000 \text{ mm}$$

So if we divide each of these equal lengths by 100, then

$$\frac{1}{100} \text{ m} = \frac{100}{100} \text{ cm} = \frac{1000}{100} \text{ mm}$$

which gives $\frac{1}{100} \text{ m} = 1 \text{ cm} = 10 \text{ mm}$.

This means that there are 10 millimetres in 1 centimetre. Alternatively if you want to know how many centimetres are equivalent to 1 millimetre, you can start from the equation 1 cm = 10 mm and divide these equal lengths by ten, so

$\frac{1}{10}$ cm = 1 mm, or 1 millimetre = $\frac{1}{10}$ centimetre.

● How many centimetres are there in 350 millimetres?

○ Each millimetre is equal to $\frac{1}{10}$ cm, so we need to multiply the number of millimetres (350) by $\frac{1}{10}$ cm. So

$$350 \, \text{mm} = 350 \times \tfrac{1}{10} \, \text{cm} = \tfrac{350}{10} \, \text{cm} = 35 \, \text{cm}$$

In general, we use the abbreviations for units in all calculations, like the ones above. Within the main text, we sometimes use the full word and sometimes the abbreviation, though as the course progresses we shall use the abbreviations more frequently. Most importantly, you can also see from these examples that the abbreviations for units are both singular and plural, so m means metre or metres.

The relationships between the four units of length that have been introduced are summarized in the equations at the end of this box.

The basic SI unit of time, the second (s), will be familiar from everyday life. Longer time intervals may be measured in minutes, hours, days, or years, but these are not SI units. Shorter times are measured in smaller multiples (or sub-multiples) of the second. Thus a millisecond (ms) is one-thousandth of a second, just as a millimetre is one-thousandth of a metre.

You may have been surprised that we said that the kilogram is the SI unit for mass, rather than the unit for weight. After all, in everyday usage we talk about somebody's weight being so many kilograms. However, in scientific use the term **weight** means the downward pull on an object due to gravity — the downward pull that makes an apple fall to the ground, for example; we'll discuss this further in Block 3. This means that your weight would decrease if you went to the Moon, where gravity is only about 1/6 as strong as on Earth. Your **mass**, however, is determined by the amount of matter in your body, and, since this doesn't depend on gravity, your mass is the same wherever you are in the Universe. Weighing scales are always marked in units of mass, e.g. kilograms, so to be scientifically correct you should say that somebody has a *mass* of 55 kilograms, rather than saying that their *weight* is 55 kilograms.

Now just as the *kilo*metre is equal to *one thousand* metres, so the *kilo*gram is equal to *one thousand* grams, 1 kilogram = 1 000 grams. You will have seen the number of grams quoted on all kinds of packaged food. Very small quantities are measured in milligrams, where one milligram (mg) is one-thousandth of a gram, 1 milligram = $\frac{1}{1000}$ gram. So, using abbreviations, 1 kg = 1 000 g, and 1 mg = $\frac{1}{1000}$ g.

Question 3.1 Complete the blanks in the following relationships between units:

(a) 5 km = ... m = ... cm = ... mm

(b) .... kg = 3 000 g = ... mg

(c) 25 s = ... ms ◀

Before we leave the discussion of units there is one other important point to remember about the relationship between units. Suppose you had to add together 100 cm and 2 m, what would be the first step you would need to take? You would convert 100 cm to 1 m, so the calculation becomes 1 m + 2 m = 3 m. Alternatively you would convert 2 m to 200 cm, so 100 cm + 200 cm = 300 cm.

The same is true for all units, not just the units of length. We shall give further help with converting units at later stages in the course.

Question 3.2 Try the following calculations, which all involve changes to units:

(a) 7 kg + 4 000 g;

(b) 55 cm − 40 mm;

(c) 20 s − 1 000 ms. ◀

Relationships between km, m, cm and mm

$$1\,km = 1\,000\,m = 100\,000\,cm = 1\,000\,000\,mm$$

$$\frac{1}{1000}\,km = 1\,m = 100\,cm = 1\,000\,mm$$

$$\frac{1}{100\,000}\,km = \frac{1}{100}\,m = 1\,cm = 10\,mm$$

$$\frac{1}{1\,000\,000}\,km = \frac{1}{1000}\,m = \frac{1}{10}\,cm = 1\,mm$$

We quoted the result of one particular measurement of the water content of cabbage leaves, in which 800 g of cabbage leaves were found to contain 700 g of water. But if a series of experiments were done to determine the water content of cabbage leaves, then it is unlikely that each experiment would start with exactly the same mass of raw cabbage leaves, and so it is probable that we would end up with a different dry mass each time. In each case there would be a different mass of water in the leaves. However, it is generally not the mass of water that is really of interest, but the fraction, or better still the percentage, of the leaves that is water.

● If 800 g of cabbage leaves are slowly dried in an oven, and then found to weigh only 100 g, what fraction of the original mass of the leaves was water? What percentage was water? (You may wish to refer back to Box 2.4.)

○ Since the 800 g of leaves lost 700 g of water when they were dried, the fraction that was water is $\frac{700\,g}{800\,g}$, which after cancelling out the zeros and the units is the same as $\frac{7}{8}$. To express this as a percentage you multiply the fraction by 100%. Thus the percentage of water is $\frac{7}{8} \times 100\% = \frac{700\%}{8}$. If you work this out in your head or with a calculator, you should get 87.5%.

This number, 87.5, is a decimal number — the first time we have introduced a decimal number — and Box 3.2, *Decimal numbers and decimal places*, reviews the important points about this type of number.

Note that the boxes are listed in the index at the end of the book. This may be the quickest way of locating the page on which a particular box starts, should you wish to refer back to one at any point.

Box 3.2 *Decimal numbers and decimal places*

Science — and, indeed, everyday life — is frequently concerned with numbers that are not whole numbers. We introduced fractions in the previous section, and a fraction like $\frac{1}{2}$ can also be written as 0.5. The number 0.5 is an example of a **decimal number**. Decimal numbers are important as calculators use them in any calculation not involving whole numbers. They are used throughout science, and you need to become proficient at adding, subtracting, multiplying and dividing decimal numbers. Fortunately your calculator will take the pain out of the calculations, so you can concentrate on understanding what the numbers mean.

Decimal numbers consist of two parts separated by what is called a **decimal point**. When printed, a 'full stop' is used for the decimal point. Here are four examples, with words in brackets indicating how you say the numbers: 0.5 ('nought point five'), 2.34 ('two point three four'), 45.875 ('forty-five point eight seven five'), and 234.76 ('two hundred and thirty-four point seven six'). Note that the part of the number before the decimal point is spoken as a whole number, and the part after the point is spoken as a series of individual digits. It's also worth noting that in parts of Europe outside the UK, a comma is used instead of a full stop in decimal numbers.

What do these numbers mean? Well, the part of the number before the decimal point represents a whole number, and the part after the decimal point represents the fraction, something between nought and one, that has to be added on to the whole number. Thus if you divide 13 by 2 you get $6\frac{1}{2}$ if you use fractions, but 6.5 if you use a calculator; the 0.5 is equivalent to the half. Note that when there is no whole number, i.e. the number is less than one, it is usual to print or write a zero in front of the decimal point, otherwise the decimal point might be overlooked. (Your calculator, however, may not always show the zero.) If you divide 13 by 4, then with fractions you get $3\frac{1}{4}$ and with a calculator you get 3.25, so a quarter is the same as 0.25.

Conversion of any fraction to a decimal number is straightforward with a calculator. All you have to do is to divide the number on the top of the fraction by the number on the bottom. Try this for yourself with the fraction $\frac{15}{40}$. Just key in:

$$\boxed{1}\boxed{5} \div \boxed{4}\boxed{0} \boxed{=}$$

and the answer is displayed as 0.375. So $\frac{15}{40} = 0.375$.

Now just as each digit that comes to the left of the decimal point has a precise meaning that depends on where it comes in the order, so also does each digit that comes after the decimal point. These meanings are summarized in Table 3.1 for the number 7 654.321.

The 4 immediately *before* the decimal point means 4 units (or 4 ones), which is simply 4; the 5 signifies 5 tens, or 50; the 6 signifies 6 hundreds, or 600; and the 7 signifies 7 thousands, or 7 000. So 7 654 means 7 000 + 600 + 50 + 4.

In a similar way, the 3 *after* the decimal point means 3 tenths, or $\frac{3}{10}$, the 2 means 2 hundredths, or $\frac{2}{100}$, and

the 1 means 1 thousandth, or $\frac{1}{1000}$. And, just as 7 654 means 7 thousands plus 6 hundreds plus 5 tens plus 4 units, so 0.321 means 3 tenths plus 2 hundredths plus 1 thousandth. So

$$0.321 = \frac{3}{10} + \frac{2}{100} + \frac{1}{1000}$$

Now, to add fractions, we first have to convert them to equivalent fractions *with the same number on the bottom*. In this case, we shall convert the first two fractions to equivalent fractions with 1 000 on the bottom.

Since $\frac{3}{10}$ is an equivalent fraction to $\frac{300}{1000}$, and $\frac{2}{100}$ is equivalent to $\frac{20}{1000}$, then

$$0.321 = \frac{300}{1000} + \frac{20}{1000} + \frac{1}{1000} = \frac{(300+20+1)}{1000} = \frac{321}{1000}$$

Here we have added the numbers on the tops of the fractions together to get the total number of 'thousandths', but we don't add the numbers on the bottoms of the fractions since these just tell us that we are adding 'thousandths' in each case.

This shows that converting a decimal number to a fraction is really quite straightforward; you just take the numbers after the decimal point (321 in the example above) and divide by 1 followed by the same number of zeros as there were digits after the decimal point (three in this case), so

$$0.321 = \frac{321}{1000}$$

A calculator does arithmetic with decimal numbers in the same way as it does with whole numbers, including carrying out operations in the right order. The only difference is that you have to key in the decimal point, using the decimal point key on the calculator, at the appropriate place in decimal numbers. (The decimal point key is the one that has something looking like a 'full stop' on it.)

Table 3.1 The meaning of each digit in the number 7 654.321.

thousands	hundreds	tens	units	point	tenths	hundredths	thousandths
7	6	5	4	.	3	2	1
$7 \times 1\,000$	6×100	5×10	4×1		$3 \times \dfrac{1}{10}$	$2 \times \dfrac{1}{100}$	$1 \times \dfrac{1}{1000}$
$= 7\,000$	$= 600$	$= 50$	$= 4$		$= 0.3$	$= 0.02$	$= 0.001$
total = 7 654					total = 0.321		

As an example, try multiplying 2.36 and 43.7. To do this you press the keys in the sequence shown below:

2 . 3 6 then × then 4 3 . 7 then =

and the result, 103.132, appears in the display.

The following questions will give you some practice at working with decimal numbers and fractions.

Question 3.3 Convert the following fractions to decimal numbers: (a) $\frac{1}{8}$; (b) $\frac{1}{4}$; (c) $\frac{3}{4}$; (d) $\frac{1}{10}$; (e) $\frac{2}{10}$; (f) $\frac{3}{10}$; (g) $\frac{1}{100}$; (h) $\frac{3}{100}$; (i) $\frac{5}{100}$; (j) $\frac{3}{1000}$. ◀

Question 3.4 Convert the following decimal numbers to fractions, and convert each fraction to the smallest whole number on the top and the bottom: (a) 0.7; (b) 0.8; (c) 0.2; (d) 0.22; (e) 0.222. ◀

Question 3.5 Work out the following decimal calculations: (a) 1.35 + 12.76; (b) 24.31 − 13.94; (c) 3.05 × 2.2; (d) 499.56 ÷ 27.6. ◀

Decimal places

So far in this box you have met decimal numbers with one, two or three digits after the decimal point. The number of digits after the decimal point is termed the *number of places of decimals*. For example, we say that the number 1.735 is expressed to three **decimal places**. 7 is in the first decimal place, 3 in the second decimal place and so on.

Now often when you do a calculation your calculator will display an answer with perhaps 7 decimal places — for example, it will indicate that $\frac{1}{3}$ is 0.333 333 3. (Note the convention of leaving a gap after every third digit after the decimal point in the same way that a gap is left every third digit before the decimal point, counting from the decimal point in each direction.) In most cases all of these digits aren't very meaningful. We might be happy to know that $\frac{1}{3}$ is about 0.33, and to forget about the thousandths and the ten-thousandths and so on. Or

sometimes it is enough to know that $\frac{1}{3}$ is about 0.3. If we approximate in this way, we say that we are **rounding** the number. But rounding is a bit more complicated than just chopping off the unwanted digits.

If we wanted to round 1.264 5 to two decimal places, we would need to look at the first digit to be removed — 4 in this case. If the first digit removed is a 0, 1, 2, 3 or 4, then the last remaining digit — 6 in this case — is *left unchanged*. So the answer would be 1.26.

However, if the first of the digits that are removed is a 5, 6, 7, 8 or 9, then the last remaining digit is *increased by one*. So, for example, if 1.264 5 is rounded to one decimal place, the answer is 1.3 — the 2 is rounded up to 3 because the first digit removed was 6.

The reason for rounding up when the first digit removed is 5 or greater is clear if you bear in mind that the number that is midway between 1.2 and 1.3 is 1.25 (since 1.2 is $1 + \frac{20}{100}$, 1.25 is $1 + \frac{25}{100}$ and 1.3 is $1 + \frac{30}{100}$).

So all numbers between 1.25 and 1.3 are closer to 1.3 than they are to 1.2. It therefore makes sense to round up the last remaining digit whenever it has been followed by a digit between 5 and 9. By convention, the digit 5 is always rounded up.

Sometimes rounding a decimal number will produce a zero as the final digit; for example, both 1.803 and 1.798 become 1.80 when rounded to two decimal places. Don't be tempted to ignore the final zero in these cases though, because it contains important information about the decimal number. Quoting a length as 1.80 m tells you that the measurement is between 1.795 0 m and 1.804 9 m because numbers within this range are equal to 1.80 m when rounded to two decimal places. Quoting the length as 1.8 m, on the other hand, means that it is between 1.750 m and 1.849 m, which is a much larger range.

Question 3.6 Round each of the following numbers to one decimal place, to two decimal places, and to three decimal places: (a) 0.264 8; (b) 0.825 51; (c) 21.118 4. ◀

Measurements of the percentage of water in cabbage leaves demonstrate that this type of plant material contains a very large proportion of water: the value we calculated earlier was 87.5%. But how typical is this value? Does all vegetable matter contain such a large percentage of water? To extend your understanding of water content, you should now do an experiment to find out the percentage of water in a potato. The potatoes that we eat are tubers, enlarged parts of the stem that grow underground, so your experiment will give an indication of whether tubers and leaves contain different percentages of water.

Before tackling this experiment, write down your best estimate, or guess, for the percentage of water that you think potatoes contain. When you have completed your experiment, you will have a measured percentage, and you will be able to compare this with your initial estimate.

Estimate/guess of the percentage of a potato that is water: ....

Measured percentage of a potato that is water: ....

Activity 3.2   How much water is there in potatoes?

One of the key activities of scientists is performing experiments to discover more about the natural world. In this first experiment in the course you will measure the water content of some potatoes, and this activity will introduce a variety of skills associated with practical work. Remember that detailed notes are in the Study File. ◄

Activity 3.3   Reviewing the potato experiment

On completing an experiment, it is good practice to review what you have done and this activity will help you to do this. It includes a video of a group of students discussing their experiences with the potato experiment. ◄

Activity 3.1   Planning your study (continued)

Make sure your log of the time spent studying Section 3 is up to date at this point. ◄

3.2   How much water?

The result of your measurement of the percentage of water in a potato may have surprised you. By far the largest component of a potato is water, though the percentage of water in a potato is smaller than in cabbage leaves. Are these two results typical of plant matter, or do other plants have quite different water contents? And how do the water contents of animals compare with those of plants? These are questions that we shall answer in this section.

First, let's look at some results from an experiment with different plant material, namely a cucumber. Cucumbers are commonly referred to as vegetables because they are not particularly sweet, but they contain seeds, just like an apple, and therefore a biologist would classify them as fruit.

● Do you think that the percentage of water in a cucumber is higher or lower than in a potato? Explain why.

○ Cucumber is very moist and almost slimy, which suggests that its water content is higher than that of a potato.

An experiment to determine the water content of cucumber was carried out with a microwave oven, using the method suggested in the notes for Activity 3.2. The results obtained were initially recorded in a table, but there is an alternative way of displaying the results. Scientists often choose to present their results as a graph. With a graph, it is usually much easier to take in the general pattern of the measurements than it is with a table of data. This is because graphs give a direct picture of the relationship between measured quantities (between mass of cucumber and time, for example). But before looking at a graph that shows the results of an experiment to measure the percentage of water in a cucumber, you should study Box 3.3, *Reading information from graphs*, which reviews the main features of graphs.

Box 3.3 Reading information from graphs

Graphs are often used to display numerical information, but in order to read this information you need to be familiar with the language of graphs. We introduce the basic vocabulary in Figure 3.1, which shows the height of an individual at different ages. This is the sort of information that you may have gathered yourself at some time, though you may not have displayed it as a graph. Study the detailed comments on this figure carefully.

○ What do you notice about the difference between adjacent numbers on the vertical scale and about the distance between the points on the scale to which they relate?

○ Adjacent numbers differ by 20 — they differ by equal amounts — and the points on the scale are separated by equal distances. So the scale in this graph is uniform; 1 cm separation between two points in the vertical direction always corresponds to a difference of 20.

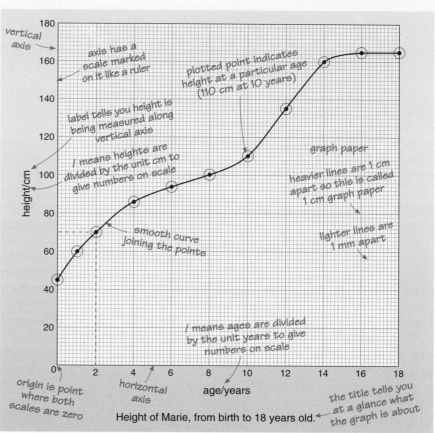

Figure 3.1 How to read information presented in graphs.

The combination of the label and the scale on the vertical axis tells us that the numbers correspond to height in centimetres, that is, 0 cm, 20 cm, 40 cm, etc. So as we move vertically upwards on the graph, the girl's height increases by 20 cm for each 1 cm on the graph paper. Now a metric ruler or tape measure marked with centimetre and millimetre divisions will normally only show numbers corresponding to the centimetre divisions of the scale, but one can make measurements to the nearest millimetre using the un-numbered intermediate lines on the scale. In the same way, the scale on a graph can be used to read

information more accurately than to the nearest number printed on the scale.

Look at Figure 3.2, which shows an enlarged version of the small section of the vertical scale between 20 and 40 cm on Figure 3.1. Because the horizontal lines on the graph in Figure 3.2 are equally spaced, we can work out what values of height correspond to each of the lines. The difference between 20 (cm) and 40 (cm) is 20 (cm), and since this 20 (cm) difference has been divided into 10 small equal divisions by the horizontal lines, then each small division represents $\frac{20\,\text{cm}}{10} = 2$ cm. So

the horizontal lines on the enlarged graph have been marked 22, 24, 26, and so on. The point on the axis indicated by arrow A corresponds to 28 cm, and the point indicated by arrow B corresponds to 36 cm. A point that is halfway between the lines marked 34 and 36 corresponds to 35 cm.

The horizontal axis in Figure 3.1 has a scale numbered 0, 2, 4, 6, … 18; these numbers correspond to the age in years. The successive numbers are separated by 1 cm, so this is also a uniform scale. For every 1 cm that we move from left to right on the graph, the age of the girl increases by 2 years.

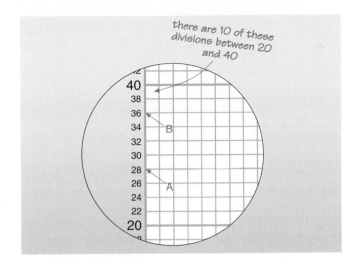

there are 10 of these divisions between 20 and 40

Figure 3.2 Enlarged part of the vertical scale of Figure 3.1

● How much does the age of the girl increase for each small division?

○ Since 10 small divisions represent 2 years, one small division (1 mm) represents $\dfrac{2\ \text{years}}{10} = 0.2$ years (which is about $2\frac{1}{2}$ months).

The combination of title, axes, axis labels, scales and graph paper give a framework for displaying the results of measurements, and these are represented by the circled points on the graph in Figure 3.1. The position of a point on the graph represents a pair of related measurements; the horizontal position of a point represents the girl's age, and the vertical position corresponds to her height *at that age*.

To work out the height for a particular point, you draw a horizontal line from the point to the vertical axis, and read off the appropriate number from the scale.

● What was the height for the third point from the left on the graph in Figure 3.1?

○ 70 cm; you find this value by drawing a line horizontally from the third point to the vertical axis, as shown in Figure 3.1.

The corresponding age is read by drawing a line vertically downwards from the point to the horizontal axis.

● What was the age for the third point from the left in Figure 3.1?

○ 2 years; you find this value by drawing a line vertically downwards from the third point to the horizontal axis, as shown in Figure 3.1.

An alternative to drawing lines on the graph is to lay a ruler on the graph, horizontally or vertically, to help your eye follow a line from a point on the graph to the axis.

● What was Marie's height at age 4 years?

○ 86 cm; to find the height, you first locate 4 years on the horizontal axis, you lay the ruler on a vertical line up to the point on the graph, and from this point you lay the ruler on a horizontal line to meet the vertical axis; you then read off the height from the point where this horizontal line meets the vertical axis.

The eleven circled points on the graph represent eleven measurements of the girl's height at different ages. The points have been joined together with a smooth curve to represent the overall trend of the measurements, and this gives an immediate visual picture of how the height changed.

● What is the trend of the girl's height with increasing age?

○ The girl's height increased rapidly in the first couple of years, and her growth then slowed down — the curve becomes flatter. There was another growth spurt corresponding to the onset of puberty, between 10 and 14 years, and her height then remained almost constant at about 165 cm. (This last height is $2\frac{1}{2}$ divisions above 160 cm, and since each division is 2 cm, the height must be $2\frac{1}{2} \times 2\ \text{cm} = 5\ \text{cm}$ above 160 cm.)

The smooth curve allows us to *estimate* the height of the girl at ages between those at which the actual measurements were made. So to estimate her height at 7 years, we find 7 years on the age axis, follow a vertical line upwards from here to the curve, and then follow a horizontal line left from this point on the curve to the vertical axis, and read the appropriate value for the height from the scale on the axis; it's about 97 cm. This process of determining intermediate values between the measurements, that is between the plotted points, is known as **interpolation**.

Question 3.7 To practise reading graphs, study Figure 3.3 and answer the following questions.

(a) What is the subject of this graph?

(b) What quantity is plotted on the vertical axis, and in what unit is it measured?

(c) What is plotted on the horizontal axis, and in what unit is it measured?

(d) What was the water flow of the stream at 12.00 hours?

(e) What is the maximum water flow of the stream and at what time did it occur?

(f) Describe in words the way that the water flow changed over the period plotted on the graph. ◀

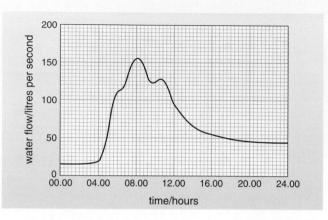

Figure 3.3 The volume of water in a stream flowing past a fixed point per second, during a flood after heavy rainfall. This is the type of graph produced by a continuously recording instrument so there are no individual plotted points.

Now you are familiar with graphs, study Figure 3.4 which shows the results of an experiment to determine the water content of a cucumber. On this graph, time is plotted horizontally in the unit of minutes and mass is plotted vertically in the unit of grams. The measured values of the cucumber's mass at various times are represented by the points, and a smooth curve has been drawn through these points. The curve shows at a glance that the mass decreases fairly steadily as the time increases for the first 15 minutes, and then it becomes almost constant after about 20 minutes. This is probably similar to the pattern for the change in mass that you observed in the potato experiment.

Question 3.8 Use the graph in Figure 3.4 to work out (a) the mass of the cucumber after 6 minutes, and (b) how long it took for the mass of the cucumber to fall to 82 grams. ◀

The graph in Figure 3.4 shows that there is a large drop in the mass of the cucumber as the water is driven out. However, to make a comparison with the results of the potato experiment, you need to determine the *percentage* of water in the cucumber, and you can do this next, using information from the graph.

Question 3.9 (a) From Figure 3.4 determine the initial mass of the cucumber, the mass of the dried cucumber and hence the mass of water in the cucumber.

(b) From these values determine the percentage of the mass of the cucumber that is water. ◀

You have now determined values for the percentages of water in potato, cabbage and cucumber, the first from your own experiment and the other two from the data in this book. The water contents of a selection of other vegetables and fruit are shown in Table 3.2 for comparison, and there are spaces there for you to write in the three values that you have determined. Also shown are values for the water content of a number of animals. The information in the table shows that, apart from peanuts and weevils, all of the organisms listed contain over 60% water, and lettuce and jellyfish contain 95% or more. Clearly water really is a major component of living organisms.

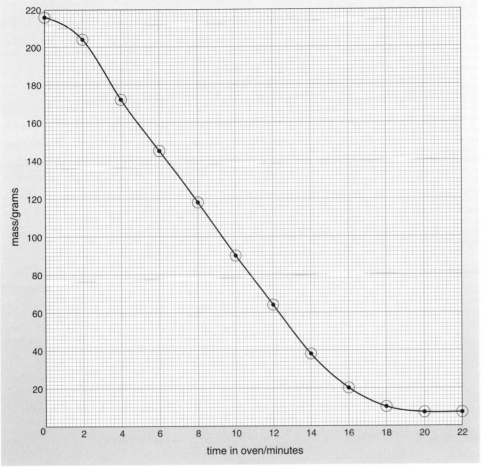

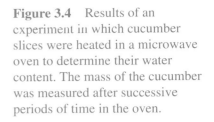

Figure 3.4   Results of an experiment in which cucumber slices were heated in a microwave oven to determine their water content. The mass of the cucumber was measured after successive periods of time in the oven.

Table 3.2   Water content of various plants (or parts of plants) and animals.

Plant	Water content/ % total mass	Animal	Water content/ % total mass
lettuce	96	jellyfish	95
tomato	93	codfish	82
strawberry	89	earthworm	80
parsnip	83	frog	78
banana	71	chicken	74
apple	65	herring	67
peanut	5	dog	63
cabbage		cockroach	61
potato		bean weevil	48
cucumber		human	

Let's now consider the human animal again, and ask what percentage of water *we* contain. Of the animals listed in Table 3.2, we are most like dogs, since humans and dogs are mammals — the scientific term for the class of animals that have fur (or hair) and milk-producing mammary glands for suckling their young. You might expect therefore that our water content would be similar to the water content of a dog. This expectation is confirmed by the available data: the typical water content of humans is about 65%, and you may want to enter this value in the table.

Of course, this value of 65% of the total mass for the water content of humans is a value for the whole body. We have seen how different parts of plants contain different percentages of water, and the same is true for our bodies. The 'driest' parts of the body are hair, containing 3% water, and tooth enamel, containing 4%, and the parts with the highest percentages are the grey matter of the brain and the testes, which each contain about 84% water, and blood, which is 83% water. In between these are bone with about 50% water, muscle with 76% and most other body tissues with between 70% and 80%.

Activity 3.4 *Constructing a table of data*

Constructing tables to display information in a concise way is an important skill that you will develop during this course, and we introduced a number of important points about tables in Box 2.2. The information in the previous paragraph about the water content of various parts of the human body is buried among a lot of words. In this activity you will construct a table that displays this information more clearly. ◄

The overall percentage of water in the body varies even in a healthy individual. For example, think of a person who goes to the pub and rapidly downs 4 litres of beer (about 7 pints of a liquid that is 95% water) without losing water by sweating or urinating. The percentage of water in their body will increase temporarily by about 1.5%, but a healthy person will rapidly get rid of even this large excess of water. In certain circumstances, however, the rapid intake of large amounts of water can have fatal effects. For example, in the mid-1990s, there were a number of tragic cases of teenagers who died after they had taken a drug at parties and had then drunk large amounts of water to avoid becoming dehydrated. The cause of death was excess water in the body, which caused the brain to swell so that it was 'crushed' within the skull. The drug was indirectly responsible because it inhibited the kidneys from getting rid of the excess water in the normal way.

There are a variety of medical conditions that result in abnormal amounts of water being retained by the body tissues. The medical term for this water retention is oedema (pronounced 'oh-dee-ma'), and it results in swelling of the body. It is an unwelcome complication of pregnancy for some women, and, among other things, is also a possible result of kidney disease.

Our friend Bones must also have been about 65% water when she was alive about 4 000 years ago. However, the water has long since disappeared from her body. All of the soft tissues have completely disappeared — food for a variety of organisms — and only the bones remain. And the bones have become dehydrated too in the hot dry ground; the water has escaped, just as it did from the potato in your experiment, so that the bones no longer contain the 50% of water that would have been present when Bones died.

3.3 Camels and cacti

Activity 3.5 Identifying key points

At the beginning of Section 3 we recommended that as you read you try to identify key points and highlight or underline them. You might have found this difficult at first. This activity is designed to help you develop this technique. ◀

Two living organisms that are associated in many peoples' minds with hot, dry deserts are camels and cacti (see the title page of this book). Camels — often referred to as 'ships of the desert' — are mostly confined to Arabia, North Africa, India and Central Asia. Cactus plants, of which there are about 1 000 different kinds, are mostly native to North America, particularly the desert areas in the southwest of the United States and in Mexico. In common with all other living organisms, camels and cacti need water to sustain life, but they can get very little of it in the desert regions in which they live. Moreover, the problems associated with the lack of water are made worse in some deserts by the extreme heat during the day.

◉ What might be the consequence of the high air temperatures for living organisms?

○ They may lose water from their surfaces, for example, by sweating in the case of animals.

Hence, to survive in deserts, organisms not only have to be able to manage for long periods without water but also have to ensure that water loss from their surfaces is kept to a minimum. So how do they cope with these conditions? Let's consider cacti first.

Cacti are very efficient at storing water in their thick, fleshy stems. For this reason they are often described as succulents, meaning 'juicy and fleshy'. A barrel cactus, like the large one shown on the title page, with a height of 1 m and a width of 0.8 m, can readily release up to two litres of drinkable water! On the infrequent occasions when rain falls in the desert, cacti use an extensive system of shallow roots (Figure 3.5) to take up water very rapidly before it can run away or evaporate. As well as having very effective water collection and storage systems, cacti also are highly efficient at conserving their stored water. Their surface layer is exceptionally waterproof. Most other types of plants have leaves which lose large amounts of water from their surfaces in hot dry conditions. But in cacti the leaves are reduced to spines or bristles; this not only minimizes water loss but the spines also protect the cacti from being grazed by animals.

We shall now consider camels, which are famous for their ability to make long, arduous journeys across waterless deserts. Camels conserve water by a number of mechanisms. Unlike humans, camels do not sweat very much. Before they start to sweat, their body temperature can rise by about 2 degrees centigrade (or Celsius) — an increase in temperature that would produce a severe fever in humans. When humans sweat most of the water comes from their blood. If the lost water is not replenished, the blood becomes too viscous (thick), and the heart has difficulty pumping it around the body. In contrast, the water lost when camels sweat comes from throughout the body tissue, and only small amounts come from the blood. To understand the significance of this, consider the following values. When humans lose 4% of their body mass through sweating, their blood volume is reduced by 10%. However, when camels go without water for a long period, they can lose about 20%

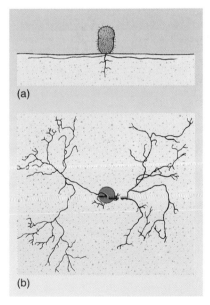

(a)

(b)

Figure 3.5 The shallow but extended root system of a barrel cactus, (a) viewed from the side, and (b) viewed from above. In each diagram the sand has been 'removed' to expose the root system.

of their body mass before their blood volume is reduced by 10%. In other words, compared with humans, camels have to lose a five times greater percentage of their body mass before their blood volume drops by 10%. Also, humans will be near death if they lose body water equal to about 12% of their body mass, but camels can survive a loss of body water equal to 40% of their body mass.

Another way in which camels conserve water is by excreting relatively small amounts of water as urine and in their faeces. Urination is the way in which various waste products leave the body dissolved in water, and it's also the way that the body eliminates any excess amounts of water. To minimize water loss, desert animals produce urine that is very concentrated — typically it contains less than half as much water for a given quantity of waste material as human urine. Faeces are solid waste products, but they do contain a certain amount of water. The faeces produced by desert animals are generally very dry.

As well as minimizing the amounts of water they lose from their bodies, camels can quickly replace any water lost by drinking enormous quantities — over 100 litres at a time — when it is available. However, they do not drink more than is required to make up the amount of water they have lost.

Camels also get part of their water intake from their food, but in addition they have remarkable humps, which are rather like portable larders. It is important to note that these humps are fat stores, *not* water tanks as many people think. When a camel is starved, it breaks down fat from its hump (just as humans break down fat when starved or dieting), and water is produced in this process, as well as energy being released.

What has emerged from this brief discussion of camels and cacti is that water is just as essential for their continued life as it is for humans. They contain similar percentages of water to other organisms, but they have characteristics that enable them to live in hot, dry desert environments, where water is not available all of the time. The observation that different types of animals and plants are adapted to different environments is one of the wonders of science, and this is a topic that we shall return to on a number of occasions during the course.

Activity 3.5   Identifying key points (continued)

You have been highlighting, or underlining, words and phrases in Section 3.3 that reveal how cacti and camels obtain, store and conserve water. Now compare your highlighted words with the ones we suggest in the comments on this activity. ◀

3.4   Summary of Section 3

All living organisms contain water. Whole plants and whole animals generally contain over 60% water, and some contain as much as 95%. The human body contains about 65% water, but there is a wide variation between the percentages of water in different parts of the body.

Some animals and plants are adapted to living in hot, dry desert environments. They minimize water loss and are very efficient at taking in water when it is available.

Scientific measurements are made using SI units. The basic SI unit for length is the metre (m), for time it is the second (s), and for mass it is the kilogram (kg). It is often convenient to use multiples and sub-multiples of the basic SI units; these larger and smaller units are indicated by prefixes to the name and symbol of the basic unit and are also regarded as SI units.

Decimals are a way of representing numbers that involve fractions. The number of digits after the decimal point is known as the number of decimal places.

Carrying out experiments (including planning, measuring, recording and analysing data, and critical evaluation) is an important part of scientific inquiry.

Graphs give a pictorial representation of the relationship between two sets of numbers, and are frequently used by scientists to display results of experiments. They show up any trends in the results.

Highlighting the text keeps your reading active and helps you to follow the argument.

Activity 3.1   *Planning your study (continued)*

You should now review your work plan and the time log you have been completing for Section 3. This will help you plan how to tackle Section 4. ◀

4 Properties of water

We are now going to broaden our view of water to include the solid and gaseous forms, ice and water vapour, both of which play important roles in the story of life. We shall look in some detail at the floating of ice on water, the evaporation of water to form water vapour, and the capacity of water to dissolve substances, and at the consequences for living organisms. Then at the end of the section we shall look at the overall recycling of water that occurs on Earth — the water cycle.

Most of the study time for this section will be dedicated to learning about important properties of water and their significance for life. However, you will also develop more maths skills, particularly those relating to calculating areas, volumes and densities, and you will learn more about effective study and the use of diagrams. Because this section contains more scientific concepts than previous ones, you may need to spend more time on it than you did on the previous sections.

Scanning a section

The previous two paragraphs have given a brief overview of the science and skills covered in this section, and you will find that there are similar 'introductions' at the start of each major section in this book. But to give yourself a more complete view of what a section contains, we recommend that you quickly scan through it before studying it more thoroughly. Your aim should be to identify the main topics and the key ideas. You should skip over the questions and activities, and not worry about highlighting or making notes. Pay particular attention to the first and last paragraphs in each section (e.g. Section 4.1, Section 4.2, etc.) because these will often give a good indication of what the sections are about. Make sure that you read the summary at the end of Section 4 too, since this will contain the most important points. As you are scanning the section, you may find it helpful to note down in your Study File the main topics, and to mark any of these that look particularly straightforward or difficult.

Activity 4.1   Reading to learn: scanning a section

So scan through Section 4 now, and note down the main topics before you start to study the section in detail. ◄

Active reading: making notes

In Section 3 you were introduced to the idea of thinking actively about the text as you read it. We suggested that you keep asking yourself 'what are the key points of this section?' and that you highlight (or underline) the important ideas in the book as you are studying. Another activity that most students find helpful is making notes as they are reading. These notes might include examples that illustrate what is being discussed in the text, thoughts that you have as you read that help you understand the arguments presented, connections with other topics that you have studied, or something that helps jog your memory. It is also very useful to make a note of parts of the text that you don't understand, so that you can come back to re-study them later, or can discuss them with other students or your tutor. Of course, the 'notes' that you make don't just have to be words; your own sketches and diagrams are equally valuable ways of recording your thoughts and responses to the text. We give help with this in a later section. You will find that your notes are extremely valuable when you come back to a section at a later stage in the course, particularly when you need to answer assignment questions.

The margins of the book are generally the best place for most notes, and if you make these notes in pencil you can erase any of them that arc no longer appropriate. For example, when the meaning of a paragraph that initially puzzled you eventually becomes clear, then you can erase your note that indicated that you didn't understand it. There will be places in the book where there isn't enough space for the notes you want to make, and you can then use sheets of paper that you file in your Study File with your responses to questions and activities. To remind yourself that you've made such notes you will probably want to write 'see Study File' at the appropriate place in the book.

Activity 4.2   Making notes as you read the text

As you study Section 4.1, highlight key points in the text and make notes in the margins, as we suggested above. When you have completed this section, you can compare your notes and highlighted phrases with a sample produced by a student. ◀

4.1   Water, ice and water vapour

The discussion in this book has so far concentrated on liquid water. That is not surprising, since the most obvious signs of the huge quantities of water on our planet are liquid — rivers, lakes, seas, oceans and rain. Moreover, when water is playing its most important roles in living organisms, it is a liquid. Indeed, the word water generally conveys a picture of a liquid. If, however, you were shivering on a polar ice-cap, the most obvious form of water all around you would be snow and ice, that is, you would see plenty of evidence for water as a *solid*. On the other hand, if you were to boil water in a kettle, you would generate **water vapour**, which is a *gas*, and if the water were left boiling for long enough, all of the liquid water in the kettle would be converted to water vapour. The hot water vapour that emerges from the spout is not visible, but it cools as it meets the cold air, and it condenses into tiny droplets of *liquid* water, rather like a hot mist or cloud (Figure 4.1). As these water droplets move further away from the spout, they evaporate to become water vapour once more.

It is worth noting in passing that scientists use the word 'steam' to describe the *gaseous* form of water. So it is steam that emerges from the spout, and it is steam that is formed again when the cloud evaporates. The intermediate stage, where you can see a cloud of tiny water droplets, is *not* steam according to the scientific use of the word. This is rather different from the everyday use of the word: most people think of the cloud of liquid water droplets as being steam, but this is not the correct scientific use of the word.

You will find examples of other words in this book that have a precise scientific meaning but that are used more loosely in everyday language (recall the use of the words *mass* and *weight* in Box 3.1). You need to be aware of the scientific meaning of such words and make sure that you use them correctly in your own writing. Newspapers quite often use scientific words incorrectly, and as you become more familiar with scientific language you will be able to spot when words are misused.

However, some scientific terms are generally used correctly in everyday language. For example, the processes of **evaporation** and **condensation**, both of which are demonstrated in Figure 4.1, are terms that refer to the changes from a liquid to a gas and from a gas to a liquid, respectively. The conversion of a liquid into a gas is also often called **vaporization**. The terms 'evaporation'and 'vaporization' are frequently used interchangeably.

droploto of hot liquid water

water vapour

Figure 4.1   Conversion of boiling liquid water to water vapour (evaporation), then to liquid water droplets (condensation).

In fact, the air around us contains water vapour all of the time. It is not visible to the human eye, so you might wonder why we are convinced that it is there. Its presence can be detected with scientific instruments, but you may be able to think of some observations or experiments that provide further evidence for the presence of water vapour in the air.

Condensation of water on cold objects is evidence for the presence of gaseous water in the air. If you take a can or bottle out of the refrigerator, drops of liquid water — condensation — will appear on its sides. This water must have come from the air. When water vapour in the air comes into contact with a cold surface, it tends to condense as liquid water on that surface. There is an important reason for this occurrence: cold air cannot hold as much water vapour as warm air. The chilled can cools the surrounding air so that it is not capable of holding as much water vapour and the 'rejected' water condenses as a liquid on the cold surface of the can. You will also have observed condensation on the inside of windows when the temperature is cold outside.

Mist, fog, clouds, rain and snow are also consequences of water vapour in the air. All are formed when moist air cools. As the air temperature falls, the air cannot hold all of the water vapour it contains and some of it condenses into very tiny droplets. If these droplets are very small, they remain suspended in the air, either as clouds if at high altitudes, or as mist or fog if near the Earth's surface.

Thus, ice, water vapour and water are different forms of one and the same substance. In science, the three different forms — **solid**, **liquid** and **gas** — are called the different **states** of substances. The observation of these three states begs several questions.

- What are the differences between the solid, liquid and gaseous states?
- Are ice, liquid water and water vapour composed of the same substance?
- What determines whether water exists as a solid, liquid or gas?

To answer these questions fully, we would have to delve prematurely into the physics and chemistry that you will meet later in the course, so for now we shall just formulate some preliminary answers.

4.1.1 Differences between solid, liquid and gaseous states

Let's think about how we might define solids, liquids and gases so that we can distinguish between them easily. A good definition of each of these three states should be applicable to any solid, liquid or gas that you can think of, but it will simplify matters if we take familiar examples of each of these states and think about their properties.

Question 4.1 By thinking of a piece of iron, some cooking oil, and the air, note down the main features of a solid, a liquid and a gas that allow each to be distinguished from the other two. It may help to think about how permanent the shapes of solids, liquids and gases are, and how easy it is to change their shape or the volume of the space they occupy. ◄

Since water is the theme of this book, let's see how our descriptions of solids, liquids and gases apply to ice, liquid water and water vapour. An ice cube has a fixed shape and volume whatever type of glass you put it in. When it melts, however, the resulting liquid water flows so that it adapts to the shape of the bottom of the glass.

However, the volume of the liquid water doesn't change when you swirl it around in the glass or when you tip it into the sink. Leave the liquid water for long enough though and it will evaporate. If this happened within a sealed room then the gaseous water would be uniformly spread out through the air in the whole room. In other words, gaseous water does not have a fixed volume — it fills any space into which it is put. This property distinguishes a gas from a liquid.

You have probably experienced the capacity of a gas to expand to fill its container without realizing it. When a person wearing perfume enters a room, you can smell the perfume almost straight away. You do not have to put your nose very close to the person wearing the perfume to get the benefit. This observation should tell you that the gas that has evaporated from the liquid perfume pervades the room very quickly.

4.1.2   Are ice, liquid water and water vapour the same substance?

How can we be sure that the liquid that we call water does not change into a different substance as water freezes into ice or as water is boiled to produce water vapour? There are various chemical experiments that prove that ice, liquid water and water vapour are all composed of the same substance, but how could you convince yourself without doing experiments?

Ice brought out of a freezer into a warm room soon turns to water, and if the water is put back into the freezer, it becomes ice again. Likewise, the substance that escapes into the air as a gas when water boils, can condense on a cold surface such as a window and become liquid water again. You could convince yourself of this by holding a cold spoon over the spout of a kettle while the water is boiling; you would soon see droplets of water on the spoon.

These changes from one state to another and back again do not demonstrate beyond doubt that ice, liquid water, and water vapour are all made from the same substance. However, scientists generally assume that *the simplest explanation of the facts is correct until some new evidence disproves it.* The fact that ice, liquid water and water vapour share a lack of colour, smell and taste is also consistent with the view that they are all the same substance.

4.1.3   What determines whether water is a solid, liquid or gas?

A major factor that determines the state of water is the temperature. When ice is brought out of a freezer, it warms up until it reaches a temperature at which the ice melts to form liquid water. If the liquid water is then heated in a saucepan, it eventually reaches a temperature at which the liquid boils, and if heated long enough it is completely transformed into water vapour. The same is true of other substances. If you heat a lump of fat and a block of iron, they will eventually reach temperatures at which they melt to become liquids, and if heated further they will boil and be converted to fat vapour and iron vapour, respectively. However, the temperatures at which ice, fat and iron melt are different, and the temperatures at which the three substances boil are all different.

So changing the temperature of a substance can lead to a change of state; but this raises more questions than it answers. For example, you may now be wondering why changing the temperature can cause the state of a substance to change, or why different substances have different melting temperatures. There is a lot more science to be discovered here, but this must wait until the next block of the course. For now, we shall just look a little more closely at the subject of temperature in Box 4.1, *Temperature scales*.

Box 4.1   Temperature scales

There are many different scales of hotness or coldness, and any of them give us a measure of temperature. Perhaps the commonest scale is degrees Celsius, abbreviated to °C, which was named in honour of a Swedish astronomer, Anders Celsius, who devised the scale in 1743. He defined the freezing temperature of water as 0 °C on this scale and the boiling temperature of water as 100 °C. The **Celsius scale** is widely referred to as the centigrade scale, because there are 100 divisions — or degrees — between the freezing and boiling temperatures of water. However, the correct scientific name of the scale is Celsius. On this scale, the normal human body temperature is around 37 °C though this varies slightly between individuals.

We now know that the freezing and boiling temperatures of water are not fixed temperatures — water boils at about 71 °C at the top of Mount Everest, for example. To define the Celsius scale we therefore have to specify more precisely the conditions under which the water freezes or melts. Thus we say that 0 °C (spoken as 'zero degrees Celsius') is the temperature at which water freezes at sea-level under normal atmospheric conditions, and this is called the *normal* **freezing temperature** of water. (Block 2 explains what we mean by 'normal atmospheric conditions'.) Similarly, 100 °C is the temperature at which water boils at sea-level under normal atmospheric conditions, and this is called the *normal* **boiling temperature** of water.

You may be more familiar with degrees Fahrenheit (°F), although this scale has largely been phased out in Britain. On the Fahrenheit scale, water normally freezes at 32 °F and boils at 212 °F, and the average temperature of a healthy human body is about 98.4 °F. In this course we shall deal mainly with the Celsius scale of temperature.

The Celsius scale is not limited to the range between 0 °C and 100 °C; for example, the temperature of the surface of the Sun is about 5 500 °C, and air temperatures frequently drop well below 0 °C in winter. When the temperature falls five degrees below 0 °C, then we say that it is minus five degrees Celsius, or –5 °C, and if it falls even further to ten degrees below zero then

it is –10 °C. Mathematically, five degrees below zero means 0 °C – 5 °C, and if you do this subtraction the answer is –5 °C, as you can easily confirm by doing the following subtraction on your calculator:

$\boxed{0} \ \boxed{-} \ \boxed{5} \ \boxed{=}$

So the minus sign in front of a temperature tells you that it is 'less than zero' and the number tells you how many degrees less than zero. In other words, the larger the number that follows the minus sign, the further the temperature is below zero degrees. (If you are not used to thinking about negative numbers, then it may help to think in terms of money. If your account is overdrawn by £50 pounds, then it has '£50 less than nothing' in it, and your balance is –£50. You would have to add £50 to bring the balance up to zero. In a similar way, if the temperature is –50 °C — that is, 50 °C 'less than nothing' — then you would have to increase the temperature by 50 °C to bring it up to zero.)

A wide range of Celsius temperatures is shown in Figure 4.2. The highest temperature we have marked is that of a hot oven. The temperatures decrease to 0 °C, and as the temperatures get still colder they are represented by negative numbers, in which the numbers following the minus sign get larger and larger. At the lowest temperature shown, –196 °C (that is 196 degrees Celsius below zero), nitrogen gas, which is the main component of the air we breathe, condenses and becomes a liquid; you will see this demonstrated in a video activity in Block 2.

Question 4.2   In each of the following pairs of temperatures, which one is the hotter: (a) 57 °C and 65 °C; (b) 57 °C and –65 °C; (c) –57 °C and –65 °C; (d) –57 °C and 65 °C? ◀

Question 4.3   Arrange the following temperatures in increasing order, i.e. starting with the lowest temperature and ending with the highest temperature: 210 °C, 0 °C, –27 °C, 1 750 °C, –85 °C, –26 °C, –210 °C, 85 °C. ◀

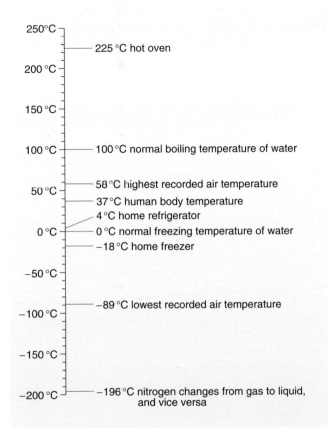

Figure 4.2 Temperatures on the Celsius scale. Note that we always use minus signs to denote negative temperatures, but we don't use plus signs in front of the positive temperatures.

The most familiar way of converting water to a gas is by heating the liquid up to the normal boiling temperature and this produces vapour at 100 °C. But liquid water does not have to be heated to its boiling temperature to convert it to gas. For example, a puddle in the road does not last forever; the water evaporates and the road becomes dry again, and the higher the temperature the more rapidly the water evaporates.

On the other hand, the most familiar way of converting water to a solid is by cooling the liquid down to below the freezing temperature, and this produces ice at below 0 °C. We look at the formation of ice in more detail in the next section.

Activity 4.2 Making notes as you read the text (continued)

We suggested that you highlighted (or underlined) parts of the text and made notes as you read this section, with the aim of identifying key points. There is an example of annotated text in the comments for this activity, and you should now compare this with what you have done. ◀

4.2 Why does ice float?

This section looks at a property of water with which you will be very familiar, but that is, in fact, exceptional and has important consequences for life. That property is illustrated by ice floating on water. Put some ice cubes in a glass of water and they float at the top; they don't sink to the bottom. On a much larger scale, icebergs float in the open seas when they break away from the ice shelf. You may never have thought of this as being particularly strange, but if you put a lump of fat into a chip pan full of melted fat then it sinks to the bottom.

Activity 4.3   Annotating text: floating and sinking

As you read Section 4.2, annotate the text to pick out information that explains why some objects float on water while others sink. You will use your annotations at the end of the section to write an explanation of why ice floats on water but a block of steel sinks in water. ◄

But how can we tell if a solid will float on a liquid? Wood floats on water, but steel doesn't. You might think that the reason for this is because steel is heavier than wood, but though that is the start of an explanation, we need to be more precise. After all, a small steel screw will sink in water but a large tree trunk will float. It isn't the mass of the steel screw that is important, it's the fact that the screw is heavier (it has a greater mass) than the amount of water that has the same volume as the screw. Conversely the tree trunk floats because it is lighter (its mass is less) than the amount of water that has the same volume as the tree trunk.

Activity 4.4   Understanding complex ideas

You will find that there are some concepts in the course that are difficult to grasp on first reading. One technique that you may find helpful in such cases is to rephrase the concept in your own words. Try doing this for the preceding paragraph, then compare your rephrasing with ours in the comments on this activity. ◄

Before looking at floating in more detail, we need to be clear about the units that are used to measure area and volume. In Box 3.1, we discussed the metric unit of mass, the kilogram (kg), and the metric unit of length, the metre (m). You may wish to refresh your memory of these units before studying Box 4.2, *Measuring areas and volumes*, which introduces the metric units of area and of volume.

Box 4.2   Measuring areas and volumes

In continental Europe, estate agents' descriptions of houses and flats always contain details of the overall area of the floor, that is, the area of a fitted carpet. In the UK this information is not a requirement; house details usually give the maximum length and width of a room, measured into bay windows and alcoves, which may give a misleading impression of the size of the room. How can you work out the floor area to give a more accurate measure of room size?

Area

For squares and rectangles, the **area** is found by multiplying the length by the width. So a simple square with 1 m long sides (Figure 4.3), has

an area of 1 m × 1 m = 1 square metre or 1 metre squared, abbreviated to 1 m². (A number written above the line and in a smaller type, as in the case of the 2 in m², is called a **superscript**. This kind of notation — using m² as a shorthand for m × m — is explained in more detail later in this block.) In SI units, area is measured in square metres.

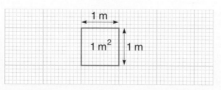

Figure 4.3   One square metre (1 m²).

The rectangular garden pond shown in Figure 4.4 has an area of 3 m × 4 m = 12 square metres (12 m²), and you can see that it is made up of 12 squares, each with sides 1 m long.

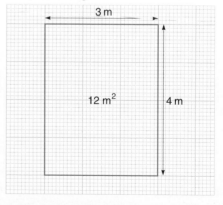

Figure 4.4   Plan of a rectangular garden pond of area 12 m².

● What is the area of a rectangular garden pond that measures 5 m × 4 m?

○ The area is 20 m².

The rectangular garden pond shown in Figure 4.5 has an area of 3.5 m × 4.2 m = 14.7 m², which you can check with your calculator. The area is still the length multiplied by the width, and if you count up 12 whole squares and eight part squares you should be able to see that the pond covers the equivalent of about 15 whole squares, each of which has 1 m side length.

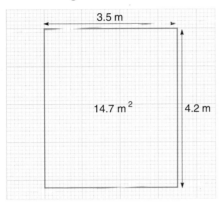

Figure 4.5 Plan of a rectangular garden pond of area 14.7 m².

● There are two ways of calculating the area of the L-shaped garden pond in Figure 4.6; can you see what these are?

○ You could think of the pond as being a large rectangle, with a smaller rectangle taken out of it, as shown in Figure 4.7a. Or you could think of it as being made up of two rectangles, so that its total area is the sum of the areas of the two parts, as shown in Figure 4.7b.

We can check that these two ways of calculating the area give the same answer.

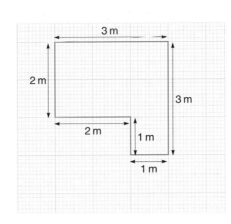

Figure 4.6 Plan of an L-shaped garden pond.

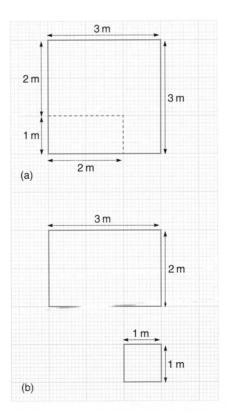

Figure 4.7 Two ways of calculating the area of an L-shaped garden pond.

Following the first method, in Figure 4.7a, the area is: 3 m × 3 m minus (or less) 2 m × 1 m. Adding brackets to a problem of this type makes it look clearer and also emphasizes the mathematical rule of carrying out the multiplying before subtracting:

$$\text{area} = (3\,\text{m} \times 3\,\text{m}) - (2\,\text{m} \times 1\,\text{m})$$
$$= 9\,\text{m}^2 - 2\,\text{m}^2 = 7\,\text{m}^2$$

If you work this out on your calculator, brackets are not essential because your calculator follows the mathematical rules and will do the multiplying before the subtracting.

Following the second method, in Figure 4.7b, the area is: 2 m × 3 m plus 1 m × 1 m, and again if we add brackets it makes the problem look clearer:

$$\text{area} = (2\,\text{m} \times 3\,\text{m}) + (1\,\text{m} \times 1\,\text{m})$$
$$= 6\,\text{m}^2 + 1\,\text{m}^2 = 7\,\text{m}^2$$

The concept of area is useful even for irregular-shaped objects; the irregular-shaped pond in Figure 4.8 has an area of about 5 square metres, and again you can verify this approximately, by counting up the metre squares and part squares.

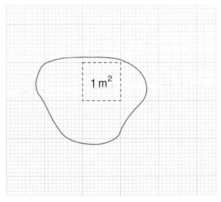

Figure 4.8 An irregular-shaped pond with an area of about 5 square metres (5 m²). The dotted square is 1 m².

Volume

The information about water use in Section 2 was given as volumes of water measured in litres, and we will now define what is meant by volume and explain how it is measured.

Volume is a measure of the space that a three-dimensional object occupies. The volume of a rectangular block is found by multiplying its length by its width by its height. A simple cube, with 1 m long sides, has a volume of $1 \, m \times 1 \, m \times 1 \, m = 1$ cubic metre, which is written as 1 m³ (Figure 4.9). In SI units, volume is measured in cubic metres.

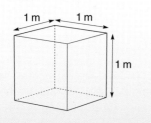

Figure 4.9 A cube with 1 m long sides and a volume of 1 cubic metre (1 m³).

The fish tank shown in Figure 4.10 has a volume of:

$3 \, m \times 2 \, m \times 1 \, m = 6$ cubic metres (or 6 m³)

and 6 cubes with 1 m sides could, in principle, be neatly stacked in the tank, as the dashed lines on the diagram indicate. For any rectangular block-like structure, such as a brick or a plank of wood, you can use the same method for measuring the volume — just multiply together the length, the width and the height, as we did for the tank in Figure 4.10.

● Suppose you had measured the dimensions of a tank in centimetres, what would be the unit of its volume?

○ The unit would be cm × cm × cm, or cubic centimetres, which is abbreviated to cm³.

However, if you had measured one dimension in mm and the other two dimensions in cm, then before calculating the volume you would have to ensure all the dimensions were in the same unit.

● What is the volume of a carton of fruit juice that has length 8 cm, width 45 mm, and height 12 cm?

○ Since 45 mm = 4.5 cm, volume of carton = 8 cm × 4.5 cm × 12 cm = 432 cm³

Unless you're in the building trade, you are probably not used to measuring volumes in cubic metres. A unit that is much more commonly used for measuring volumes of liquids is the **litre** (abbreviated to **l**). Fruit juices and emulsion paint, for example, are sold in litre volumes. A litre is the volume of a cube that has 10 cm sides.

If you think about stacking cubes with 10 cm long sides in a 1 m cube (Figure 4.11), then you can see that we would need $10 \times 10 \times 10 = 1\,000$ of the 10 cm cubes to fill a cubic metre (1 m³), so

1 000 litres = 1 cubic metre (1 m³)

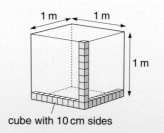

cube with 10 cm sides

Figure 4.11 How many of the small yellow 10 cm cubes could be stacked in 1 m³?

● How many cubic centimetres (cm³) are there in 1 litre?

○ A cube with 10 cm sides has a volume of 1 litre. If you think about stacking 1 cm cubes in a 10 cm cube, then you can see that there are $10 \times 10 \times 10 = 1\,000$ of the 1 cm cubes in 1 litre, so 1 000 cm³ = 1 litre.

Question 4.4 A rectangular swimming pool has the following dimensions: 6 m long by 7 m wide and 2 m deep. What is the area of the bottom of the pool and what is the volume of the pool? ◀

Question 4.5 A reservoir is known to have the capacity to store 2.5 million litres of water. How many cubic metres is this? ◀

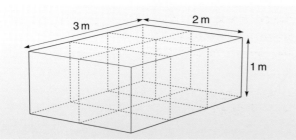

Figure 4.10 A fish tank and its dimensions.

4.2.1 Density

We can now return to our original question, 'How can we tell if a solid will float on a liquid?'. To answer this, we need to compare the mass of a particular volume of the solid, such as steel, with the mass of the same volume of water. Table 4.1 lists the masses of one cubic metre (1 m³) of a number of solids and liquids. Clearly all these materials have different masses for the same 1 m³ volume. The table shows that one cubic metre of steel has a mass of 7 800 kg, and that one cubic metre of water has a mass of 1 000 kg. The ratio of these masses is 7 800 kg : 1 000 kg, which is the same as 78 : 10 or 7.8 : 1; by using a ratio in which the smallest number is 1, you can see that the mass of the steel is 7.8 times greater than the mass of the water. So, since the mass of one cubic metre of steel is greater than the mass of one cubic metre of water, the steel will sink in the water. Conversely, one cubic metre of oak will float in water because its mass is less than that of one cubic metre of water.

Fortunately, if we want to know whether a 2 m³ steel block floats or sinks in water, we don't need to work out the mass of that block and compare it with the mass of 2 m³ of water. That's because if 1 m³ of steel has 7.8 times the mass of 1 m³ of water, then 2 m³ of steel will have 7.8 times the mass of 2 m³ of water. Similarly 10 m³ of steel will also have 7.8 times the mass of 10 m³ of water. The reason for this is that, for any material, if we double the volume, we will double the mass, and if we increase the volume ten-fold, then the mass also increases ten-fold. The mass and the volume of objects made from the same material increase and decrease in step with each other.

This close link between the masses and volumes of objects leads us to introduce a concept known as density. You may already be familiar with this concept. It is quite easy to lift a cubic metre of expanded polystyrene (the white synthetic material used for insulation and packaging), but you would need a crane to lift a cubic metre of steel. This is because there is far less mass for a cubic metre of polystyrene than for the same volume of steel. This concept of the amount of mass for a given volume is density.

Let's make this concept more precise. The **density** of any object, such as a steel screw, is defined as its mass divided by its volume, so

density *equals* mass *divided by* volume, or

$$\text{density} = \frac{\text{mass}}{\text{volume}}$$

This is a *word equation*, and it gives us a way of working out the density of any object, as long as we know the mass of the object and its volume. We simply replace the word 'mass' in the equation by the actual value of the mass of the object, and replace the word 'volume' by the actual volume.

Let's take our one cubic metre block of steel as an example. From Table 4.1 we know that the mass of this block is 7 800 kg, and the volume is 1 m³. So

$$\text{density} = \frac{\text{mass}}{\text{volume}} = \frac{7\,800\,\text{kg}}{1\,\text{m}^3} = 7\,800\,\frac{\text{kg}}{\text{m}^3}$$

Table 4.1 Mass of one cubic metre of various materials.

Material	Mass/kg
gold	19 280
silver	10 500
steel	7 800
rock (granite)	2 700
bone	1 800
water	1 000
olive oil	920
petrol	800
wood (oak)	650
expanded polystyrene	20

You will find that certain important key points and equations are highlighted in this way to emphasize them.

Notice that we included the unit of mass and the unit of volume in the equation, and we've ended up with the unit of kg/m³ — kilograms per cubic metre. This is the SI unit for density. It may look complicated, but it specifies clearly what density is measuring — the amount of mass (kg) in a certain volume (1 m³). Later in the block we shall show you another way of writing the unit of density.

The reason that this concept of density is so important is that *the density of any material doesn't depend on the size or shape of the object made from the material.* This means that the density of a steel bar is the same as the density of our 1 m³ steel block,* as you can confirm by answering the following question.

⬤   A steel bar has a mass of 234 kg and a volume of 0.030 m³. What is the density of this bar?

◯   Density = mass/volume = 234 kg/0.030 m³ = 7 800 kg/m³

So although the mass of the bar is about 30 times smaller than the mass of the steel block, its density is exactly the same as the value we calculated above for the block. What is more, a steel screw or any other object made from the same steel would also have the same density, 7 800 kg/m³. So once the density of the steel, or any other material, has been measured, we don't have to measure it again for every object that we make. We simply look up the value of the density of the material in reference tables.

Now Table 4.1 lists the masses in kilograms of a cubic metre of various materials, so the numbers in the table are in fact the same as the densities of the materials in units of kg/m³. You might, therefore, like to pencil in an alternative title for the table — 'Density of various materials' — and an alternative heading for the second column — 'Density/kg per m³'.

Before leaving this section, note the value of 0.030 m³ for the volume of the steel bar given above. Recall that the last zero in a decimal number contains important information. If you are not certain what this zero tells you, reread the last paragraph of Box 3.2.

4.2.2   Sink or float?

Earlier we said that you could tell whether a piece of steel would sink or float if you compared the mass of that piece of steel with the mass of an amount of water that has the same volume as the steel. That experimental approach to deciding whether something sinks or floats is no longer necessary if we have tables of density values available, such as Table 4.1.

If you want to know whether a material sinks or floats in a liquid, all you have to do is to compare the density of the material with the density of the liquid. If the material has a higher density than the liquid, it will sink. So, for example, steel will sink in water because its density (7 800 kg/m³) is greater than that of water (1 000 kg/m³). The mass of a cubic metre of steel is 7.8 times greater than the mass of a cubic metre of the water — so a cubic metre of steel would sink — and the mass of any other volume of steel will be 7.8 times greater than the mass of the same volume of water

YOU'RE THICK! YOU SHOULD HAVE LEARNED TO SWIM!

YOU'RE THE THICK ONE— I'M JUST DENSE !

*We are assuming that the bar and block are made from the same type of steel. There is a range of different types of steel (e.g. mild, stainless) that are manufactured from different proportions of various constituents, and the densities of the different steels vary slightly.

— so they would also sink. Similarly, you can see from Table 4.1, that the densities of gold, silver, granite and bone are very much greater than that of water; these materials will also sink in water. However, materials that have a density lower than that of water will float.

● Which of the materials listed in Table 4.1 will float on water?

○ Olive oil, petrol, wood and polystyrene will float on water because their densities are less than that of water.

The idea that a material floats or sinks in a liquid depending on whether its density is less than or greater than the density of the surrounding liquid provides the answer to the question of why ice floats on water.

● A rectangular sheet of ice on a pond has dimensions 2.5 m × 2.0 m × 0.10 m and its mass is 460 kg. What is the density of the ice?

○ The volume of the ice is 2.5 m × 2.0 m × 0.10 m = 0.50 m³, so the density of ice is 460 kg/0.50 m³ = 920 kg/m³.

Thus the density of ice is lower than that of water (1 000 kg/m³) so ice will float on top of water. Hence a pond or lake will ice over on the top.

This capacity of ice to float on water is very important for life in ponds and lakes. To understand its significance, consider what would happen if ice sank to the bottom of water. Think about a pond or lake in winter, with the air temperature below 0 °C. The surface of the water will cool down, and eventually ice will form. If this ice sank to the bottom, then more ice would form at the surface and sink, and more and more ice would form and sink. This would be a very efficient way of cooling down the pond and freezing it solid, with fatal consequences for the fish and other aquatic life. But because ice floats on water, it forms an insulating blanket on the top, which then often gets covered with a further insulating blanket of snow. Conditions have to be very much more severe before the pond will freeze completely. If ice did not float, aquatic life would be restricted to parts of the world where temperatures did not fall below freezing.

Question 4.6 What are the densities of the blocks shown in Figure 4.12? Will either of the two blocks float in water? ◄

Activity 4.3 Annotating text: floating and sinking (continued)

With the help of your highlighted phrases and notes for Section 4.2, write a few sentences explaining why ice floats on water but a block of steel sinks in water. ◄

4.3 Sweating to keep cool

In Section 4.2 we considered what happens to water when its temperature drops to 0 °C and below, causing the water to change from the liquid state to the solid state. In this section we shall look at some of the consequences of water changing from the liquid state to the gaseous state.

When the air temperature reaches 25 °C or more we feel hot and begin to sweat. You learnt in Section 3.3 that one way in which animals, including humans, lose water is by means of sweating. The real purpose of sweating, however, is not to lose water, but to cool the body. But sweating itself doesn't produce cooling. If you wrap up in

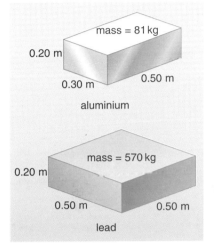

Figure 4.12 Two blocks of metal and their dimensions, for use with Question 4.6. Note that all of the dimensions are expressed to two decimal places because they were measured to the nearest centimetre (0.01 m). If the final zeros were omitted, we would assume that the dimensions were only measured to the nearest 0.1 m, or ten centimetres.

tight clothes in a hot place, then sweating doesn't cool you down. Sweat needs to be able to evaporate, and it's the evaporation of the water — the change from a liquid to a vapour — that produces the cooling effect.

In order to understand this cooling effect, let's first think about what happens when you heat water. You can do this in all kinds of ways: in an electric kettle or using various fuels — for example, gas, paraffin or wood. These all provide energy, in one form or another, and the energy they supply will raise the temperature of a kettle of water. But let's focus on an electric kettle: the temperature of the water rises steadily as the heating element in the kettle provides energy to the water. When the water reaches its normal boiling temperature, 100 °C, the temperature stops rising; it stays at 100 °C while the water boils merrily away. Energy is still being supplied to the water — your electricity meter shows this — but now, rather than raising the temperature of the water, the energy supplied is being used to convert the water to vapour, that is to evaporate it (Section 4.1). This demonstrates that it takes energy to raise the temperature of a liquid (or a solid) and it also takes energy to evaporate a liquid, and if we're using an electric kettle then the energy comes from the electricity supply.

So what is the connection between an electric kettle of boiling water and the process of sweating? Sweat on the skin will evaporate into the air. Unlike the boiling water in the kettle, the skin isn't at 100 °C, but energy is still required in order for the water to evaporate. The energy to evaporate the sweat comes from the body. We usually refer to the energy that is supplied in this way as heat, so the body has to provide heat to evaporate the sweat from the skin. The loss of heat from the surface of the body to the water vapour means that the skin cools down. This cooling effect is even more noticeable when you put perfume or aftershave on the skin; your skin immediately feels cool because it supplies heat to evaporate the liquid.

You are probably aware of applications of the principle that evaporation of water produces a cooling effect. Suppose you don't have a refrigerator and are expecting friends for a meal. You want to cool a bottle of wine or fruit juice; how would you do it? A very effective way is to put a wet towel round the bottle and put it on an outdoor window ledge. The water evaporates from the towel, and the heat required to evaporate the water comes from the bottle. So the evaporation of the water from the towel cools the wine or fruit juice in the same way that evaporation of your sweat cools you down on a hot day.

Question 4.7   Does the process of evaporation of water occur only at its boiling temperature? Give examples to support your answer, some of which might be from earlier parts of Section 4. ◀

4.4 Dissolving

So far in Section 4 we have considered some of the consequences for life, both when liquid water forms ice and when it forms water vapour. We now consider a third property of water — this time when it is in the liquid state — the fact that substances **dissolve** in water.

Put a teaspoonful of table salt in a pan of boiling water and it disappears — it dissolves. However, although the salt seems to have disappeared, in fact it is still present in the water. You can convince yourself by tasting the water. The liquid is now a **solution** of salt in water. The salt can no longer be seen because it has separated into very small particles that are dispersed in the water. If you poured the salty water onto a dinner plate and left it overnight in a warm place, the water would evaporate and the solid salt crystals would reappear, coating the bottom of the plate, and thus providing evidence that it was there all the time. This observation also reveals that dissolving is a reversible process.

Any substance that dissolves in water is said to be **soluble** in water.

 What other examples of solid substances that dissolve in water are you familiar with?

You may have thought of some of the following: sugar, bicarbonate of soda, soluble aspirin, soda crystals, washing powder, instant coffee. There are many others.

The first living organisms on Earth evolved in liquid water, and one important reason for this is that many substances needed to sustain life are soluble in water. The water-based fluids found in living organisms, such as blood, urine and sweat (Section 2.5), all contain different dissolved substances. Equally significant for life is the fact that some substances do not dissolve in water, they are **insoluble** in water. Amongst the important insoluble substances are those that form the surface layer of organisms, such as the skin of humans. Hence you don't dissolve when you take a swim!

Make a list of substances you put in water that are insoluble in water.

China and pottery (crockery), metal (cutlery), wood and plastic (utensils), cotton and wool (clothes), leather (shoes), sand, cooking oil and flowers, to name but a few.

A liquid that dissolves another substance is called a **solvent**. Water is only one kind of solvent. Oil, grease and gloss paints (which are oil-based), for example, do not dissolve in water but do dissolve in white spirit. Even white spirit will not dissolve the spray paint used on cars. It needs another kind of solvent. But no other liquid dissolves such a large variety of substances as water, which is why water is an ideal solvent for scientists, industrialists and cooks.

In order to appreciate the importance of the capacity of water to dissolve substances, we shall consider the quality of drinking water, and the fate of a glass of water when you drink it.

4.4.1 Purity of drinking water

No natural water found on Earth is pure; any sample of water contains more than just water. As you know, some solid materials, such as table salt, are very soluble and large quantities will dissolve in water, whereas other materials are less soluble. The largest natural water reservoirs on Earth are the oceans, which comprise salty water containing many valuable dissolved substances, such as sodium, calcium, magnesium and even gold. Rivers, lakes and artificial water reservoirs usually contain much less of these substances.

Not only solid substances dissolve in water; gases do too. For example, rainwater is almost pure water containing only dissolved gases from the atmosphere; it is a solution of liquid water and gases. One of the most important of these gases is oxygen, which is found dissolved in seawater, particularly near the surface, and in fresh river water. This dissolved oxygen is extracted from water by many aquatic organisms, some of which have special structures for this purpose; for example, fish have gills.

Ideally all drinking water should be of a certain quality to be acceptable for human consumption, that is, to be *potable*. It is not necessary for this water to be absolutely pure, but it is essential that it does not contain harmful materials, such as dissolved poisons, or harmful bacteria that could cause illness. The World Health Organization has set international drinking water standards for the maximum amounts of impurities in potable water.

Bacteria, of which there are many different types, are very small organisms, too small to be seen without the magnification of a microscope. They are found nearly everywhere, including the inside of your intestine, in soil and in water. Many of them are harmless and indeed can be beneficial; for example, bacteria in the soil break down dead organic material and thus stop it accumulating. However, other bacteria can cause disease in a variety of organisms, including humans. For example, drinking water contaminated with typhoid bacteria can lead to the development of typhoid fever in people who drink the water (Figure 4.13).

Figure 4.13 'Monster soup'; a cartoon of around 1830 on the quality of water from the River Thames being supplied as drinking water by the London Water Companies. Harmful bacteria in the water caused regular outbreaks of illness in London around this time.

Unfortunately, much potentially harmful waste from farming and industry is soluble, and can find its way into water supplies. An example of the former are the nitrogen-containing fertilizers that are required to support plant growth in areas of intensive farming. Rain washes some of the fertilizer from the fields into streams, rivers and underground water sources and problems arise when these fertilizers contaminate drinking water. When drunk, such contaminated water can interfere with the transport of oxygen in the blood. In the Anglian Water region, where extensive areas are devoted to agriculture, some of the underground water sources on which the region relies have nitrogen levels eight times higher than that recommended by the World Health Organization. This water has to be mixed with water from other sources that has a very low level of nitrogen, before it is piped to homes.

It would be a difficult task to make water absolutely pure on a large scale, but fortunately it isn't desirable to do this because many of the substances water contains are required in our diet. An example of one such ingredient is calcium, which is required for healthy bones and teeth. Even bottled drinking waters are not 100%

water. Have a look at the label next time you see a bottle of water, and note the amounts of calcium and other substances that it contains. The amounts of dissolved substances in two samples of bottled water are shown in Figure 4.14 for comparison. You will learn about these substances during your study of the course.

Question 4.8   Look at Figure 4.14. How many times more calcium does water (a) contain per litre than water (b)? What is the ratio of these two quantities of calcium? ◄

4.4.2   Water in the human body

It is important to realize that ingested water doesn't simply travel directly to the bladder, ready to be expelled. Water permeates the whole of the human body and it can move from one location to another by a variety of routes.

As you learnt in Section 3.2, about 65% of the human body is water. Water is a major component of all fluids in the body, and only a surprisingly small amount, about 8% of the total amount of water in the body, is found in the blood. You may recall from Section 2.5 some other essential water-based fluids in the human body. These include mucus in the lining of the lungs and nose, tears that continually bathe the eyes, saliva secreted in the mouth and various digestive juices secreted in the intestines. These fluids are localized in particular parts of the body. However, there is another important fluid in the body — tissue fluid. This fluid is found surrounding organs such as the brain, kidney, heart, and lungs, and within the tissues that make up these organs.

All living organisms are composed of small cells; indeed the cell is often referred to as the 'unit of life'. You, for example, consist of many millions of millions of cells. Cells are too small to be seen with the naked eye, but if you were to take a thin scraping from the inside of your cheek and look at it under a microscope you would see some cells, like those in Figure 4.15. The important point about cells for our theme of 'water for life' is that every cell contains water (in most cases as much as 70%) and the cell surface is also bathed by tissue fluid. Clearly water is a crucial component of all living organisms.

4.4.3   A drink of water

In this section we shall follow the journey of a glass of water through the body.

Activity 4.5   Annotating text: fluids in the body

As you read this section you should highlight and make notes on the *roles* of water-based fluids in the body — the details of the movement of water through the body are not so important. At the end of the section, we will ask you to produce a list of these fluids and their functions. ◄

Let's start in the mouth where the water is mixed with a little saliva, the role of which is to moisten and soften food and to start the digestive process. It is then swallowed to begin a journey to the stomach (shown in Figures 4.16b and c). In the stomach the water is one of many substances, eaten or drunk, that are churned and mixed together. A big muscular wave of the stomach propels the water with part-digested food through the small opening to the first section of the small intestine, called the duodenum (Figure 4.16c). Here it is joined by secretions of digestive juices with which it is mixed and is thrown from one end of the duodenum to the other as if in a cocktail shaker. As it continues its journey through the intestine, for ever being

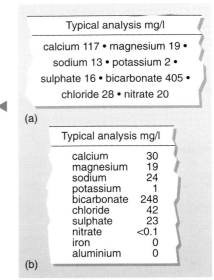

(a)

(b)

Figure 4.14   The amounts of dissolved substances in bottled water from two different areas of the British Isles. The units used are mg/l, which means milligrams of dissolved substance per litre of bottled water. The symbol < means 'less than'.

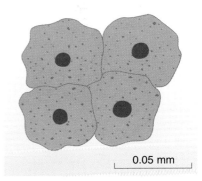

Figure 4.15   A schematic diagram of four cells from the inside of a human cheek. The scale bar shows the length on the figure that the bar represents. In this case the length of the bar is much larger than the length it represents (only 0.05 mm) and this shows that the drawing is greatly magnified. The size of a cheek cell is roughly the same size as the bar, so each cell is about 0.05 mm wide. (You will learn more about cells in Block 4.)

propelled forward, it is mixed with more digestive juices. These break down the food into smaller and smaller pieces, releasing the water content of the food into the intestine. Eventually, the mixture of water and broken-down food becomes a soft milky suspension. The soluble bits of digested food (nutrients) are taken up into fine blood vessels. The blood carries the nutrients taken up from the small intestine to the liver (Figures 4.16b and c) for storage and redistribution to other parts of the body that need them. The remaining food eventually passes into the large intestine (Figures 4.16b and c) in a watery condition. The large intestine takes up water from the liquid matter, leaving a semi-solid mixture, which is carried to the rectum (Figures 4.16b and c) to be expelled as faeces.

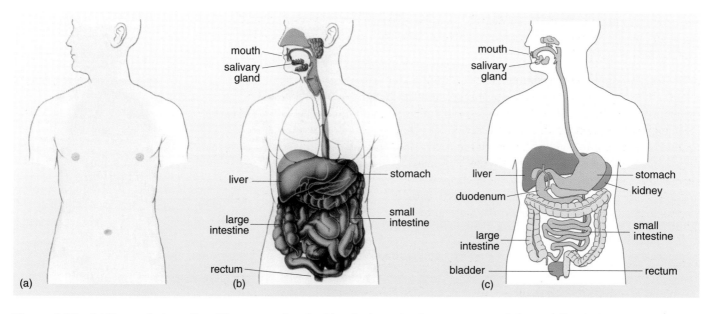

(a) (b) (c)

Figure 4.16 (a) External view of part of the human body. (b) View of some internal organs with overlying bone and tissue removed. (c) Simplified diagram of certain internal organs.

The water absorbed by the intestine becomes part of the rapidly circulating blood fluid. (If this take-up of water is interrupted, such as by the consumption of excessive amounts of alcohol, the body rapidly dehydrates.) The increased blood volume that follows the uptake of water results in the dilution of the blood. When this occurs, water filters out of the blood into the tissues and this helps to keep the blood volume constant. Some of the water transported in very fine blood vessels may reach the skin to be excreted from one of the numerous pores as sweat, carrying some waste salts with it, and cooling the body. As described in Section 3.3, the blood becomes more concentrated as a consequence of sweating, so water is then taken up from the tissues into the blood to replace the lost fluid. Hence one important function of the movement of water is the regulation of blood volume.

Some of the water leaves the blood vessels to become part of the tissue fluid, which drains into a network of fine tubes (called the lymphatic system). These tubes collect tissue fluid from around the body and return it to the bloodstream, completing the circuit. Water in tissue fluid can move into and out of cells, so when it re-enters the bloodstream it brings with it dissolved waste materials, including gases, such as carbon dioxide. Some of the water passes to the lining of the lungs where it may be lost to the outside in the moist air that is exhaled. Breathe on a mirror and tiny droplets of water condense on it to reveal that exhaled air contains water vapour.

Blood circulates to the kidneys (Figure 4.16c), where it passes through a filtering system. Not only do the kidneys regulate water balance, they also clean and filter the blood. Each day your kidneys filter about 1 900 litres of recycling blood. Excess water, along with large amounts of waste products, including salts and toxic substances, forms urine. The urine enters the bladder (Figure 4.16c) where it is stored until it is expelled.

Over a period of time, the total amount of water in the body stays about the same; that is, the amount taken in equals the amount expelled:

amount of water taken in by the body = amount of water expelled by the body

Question 4.9   Write down the substances that contribute to each side of this word equation, that is, the various substances in which the water enters the body and in which it leaves the body. ◀

Over the course of a day the amount of water in the human body fluctuates, but overall there is a balance between the amount of water consumed in a day and the amount of water lost. This is illustrated by the data in Table 4.2. The body has control mechanisms that maintain this water balance. So, for example, when the water content of your body is too low, then you feel thirsty and will find something to drink. Similarly, when the water content of your body is too high, after drinking large quantities, your body will increase production of urine to remove the excess. The data in Table 4.2 show very clearly that, on average, there is no net gain, or loss, in water content over the course of 24 hours; the amount of water taken in equals the amount lost.

Table 4.2   Approximate figures for the water balance in a human over 24 hours.

Source of water	Gain/litres	Source of water	Loss/litres
food	1.5	faeces	0.1
drink	1.0	urine	1.5
		evaporation (from sweat and breathing)	0.9
total gain	2.5	total loss	2.5

Activity 4.5   Annotating text: fluids in the body (continued)

Section 4.4.3 contains information about the water-based fluids in the human body and the functions that each performs. Use your notes and/or highlighting of the text to make a list of these fluids and their functions. ◀

Activity 4.6   Uses of illustrations

Box 2.1 introduced you to two ways in which illustrations are used in scientific writing, and to the notion of 'reading' illustrations. This activity involves you in looking a little more closely at the information illustrations contain, and at how different types of illustrations are used for different purposes. ◀

4.5   The water cycle

Most living organisms depend on rainfall for the water that they need to survive. But where does the rain come from, and where does it go to once it has fallen on the ground?

On the Earth, water is constantly moving around in what is called the **water cycle**. The cycle describes the ways in which water is transported and stored on the Earth, and illustrates the dependence of this natural cycle on the interconversion between gaseous, liquid and solid states of water, a description of which was given in Section 4.1. An important feature of this cycle is that it involves living organisms.

Activity 4.7   Annotating text: changing states of water

As you read Section 4.5, annotate the text each time a change in state is mentioned. You will use your annotations at the end of the section to review the changes in state that occur during the water cycle. ◄

We are going to follow the movement of water through the water cycle. Let's begin in one of the salty oceans where most of the Earth's water is found. This water travels thousands of kilometres in ocean currents. It may pass through the mouths and gills of fishes, or be jettisoned out of the blowholes of whales or drawn in and expelled through the 'mouth' of a jellyfish. Water at the surface of the ocean is heated by the Sun, and evaporates into the air. The process of evaporation is important, not only for the water cycle, but also because the water evaporated from the oceans is pure water. The evaporation process separates the water from all the dissolved and solid substances the oceans contain. Once in the air, the water vapour becomes part of an air stream and is carried by the wind.

Figure 4.17   A schematic diagram of the water cycle.

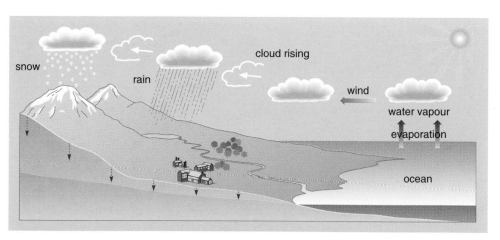

Figure 4.17 shows that some water vapour rises over the oceans and that some is blown inland and moves upwards over land masses. As the air and the water vapour it contains rises, it cools down. You may have experienced this decrease in temperature when climbing a hill or mountain. If you have ever walked up Ben Nevis, you will know that even in summer there is ice near the summit. Also, at the base of Everest there is sub-tropical vegetation; the summit is decidedly less hospitable! As the air becomes colder, some of the water vapour condenses into water droplets, which form a cloud. The process is just like the 'clouds' of condensation that form when you exhale warm air from your lungs into a cold atmosphere, an effect that is particularly noticeable on cold winter days and nights. In a cloud, the small droplets join together

to make larger droplets and eventually the droplets grow too large to be held in the air any longer and start to fall to Earth. You are, of course, familiar with the end product of this process, rain.

○ What happens to water droplets if they pass through air that is at a temperature of less than 0 °C?

○ They freeze and become hailstones.

However, if the air temperature is below 0 °C in the region where water vapour condenses, then the vapour changes directly to ice without passing through the liquid state. The ice crystals formed in this process are snow, and they are much less dense than hail. Once on the ground, a water droplet, or a thawed snowflake or hailstone, may be subject to any one of a number of different fates. Some water will soak into the soil and percolate down to the level below which the rocks are permanently wet, where it may remain for hundreds of years as underground water. Other water falling on the soil might be taken up by the roots of a tree and eventually return to the atmosphere by evaporation from the leaves, or it might run off directly into a stream or river. From a stream the water might be drunk by a cow or join other streams or lakes, and from a river the water might possibly be collected into a reservoir. Water that falls on pavements and roads in towns is likely to be transported down gutters into drains, where it might get mixed with domestic waste and taken to a sewage works. Eventually the water joins a river, and returns to the oceans, nature's largest reservoirs. And so the cycle continues.

Activity 4.7   Annotating text: changing states of water (continued)

At the beginning of Section 4.5 we suggested that you annotate the text to indicate where changes in the state of water occurred. Look back through your notes now, and list the stages at which water changes its state during movement through the water cycle. ◀

Activity 4.8   Learning from illustrations

Diagrams are a useful way of summarizing complex relationships, and Figure 4.17 has been designed to summarize aspects of the water cycle described in the text. Look carefully at Figure 4.17 and write down what it is telling you about the water cycle. ◀

4.6   Summary of Section 4

Water has three states: solid ice of fixed volume and shape; highly mobile liquid of fixed volume which flows and adapts to the shape of the container; and water vapour (a gas) with no fixed volume or shape.

On the Celsius scale, the normal freezing temperature of water is 0 °C and its normal boiling temperature is 100 °C.

Density is mass divided by volume and the SI unit is kg/m^3. Objects with a higher density than water will sink in water; objects with a lower density than water will float on water.

Sweat must evaporate in order to cool the body. It takes energy to convert liquid sweat into water vapour and this energy comes from the body in the form of heat. The loss of this heat cools the body.

Water is a powerful solvent; a huge variety of substances dissolve in it (including solids and gases).

Water permeates the whole body of a living organism, such as a human; there is an overall balance between the amount of water taken in by an organism and the amount lost.

Water is constantly being cycled on Earth.

One approach to study is to scan the text first, before studying it carefully and completing all the questions and activities.

The area of a square or rectangle is length × width and the SI unit is m^2. The volume of a rectangular block is length × width × height and the SI unit is m^3.

Illustrations convey important information by making passages of text easier to understand or by summarizing what is in the text.

Activity 4.9   Reviewing your study methods

This activity is designed to make you think about the way you studied Section 4 before moving on to Section 5. ◀

Communicating science

Communication is an important aspect of studying science. All scientists need to be able to communicate their findings to others, and the authors of this book had to use their communication skills to produce the course materials. During your study of the course you will need to be able to communicate with others, for example, by writing assignments. This is why Section 5 is devoted to writing skills, in other words how to communicate your understanding of science in writing to other people in a way that they will understand. It begins with the basics of good writing, such as sentence construction and the use of punctuation, and moves on to discuss how to put the scientific content together to produce a clearly structured piece of writing. In your study of Block 1 so far, you have already been practising your communication skills when making notes and writing responses to questions and activities. But however much practice you have had at writing, improvements can always be made, so you should study this section just as carefully as the others in this book.

Activity 5.1 Planning your study

In Activities 2.1 and 3.1 you kept a log of the time spent on study, and then reviewed your plans for finding the time for study. Before you begin to study this section we would like you to plan when and how you are going to study the remainder of this block. Again remember to keep a log of the time spent on studying this section. ◀

5.1 Thinking about writing

The skill of writing clearly and to good effect is important, not least because it is useful in many work activities and day-to-day activities. Pause for a moment and think about when you last had to write something down in order to pass on some information to someone else. Who were you communicating with? What was the information about? If you can recall it, what did you actually write?

You may have thought about a note to whoever delivers your milk, which may have read something like '3 pts today, please'. It would have been safe to assume that the recipient would realize that '3 pts' meant 'three pints of milk', and the shorthand form of your note would have been perfectly adequate to ensure three one-pint bottles (or cartons) of milk were left outside your door. Similarly, if you thought of a telephone message, then the message could have read something like 'Ring Chris Thurs eve — dinner Sat', because you were aware that whoever was going to read the note would know who Chris was, would understand that Thurs and Sat are abbreviations for Thursday and Saturday, and that 'eve' is short for 'evening'. You might even have been able to assume that the reader would realize that 'dinner Sat' referred to an invitation to dinner on a particular Saturday. In both examples, your abbreviated note would have been intelligible to the person who had to read it because the background to what you were saying would be fully understood.

When it comes to writing more formal letters, then the same shorthand won't do. If you were writing to a child's teacher, for example, to explain the child's absence from school due to illness, then your note is likely to require rather more than 'Pat tummy-bug Tues, Wed', scribbled on a scrap of paper. If you wanted some information from your bank about your account, the bank would require full details of your account number, and the nature of your query before releasing information. If you want the bank to provide you with the information you actually want, then your letter must be clear, and contain the appropriate information.

In the same way, the sort of shorthand notes you might make as reminders in the margins of this book, or in your Study File, are likely to be meaningful only to yourself. But when you communicate your understanding by writing assignments, you will have to make it quite clear to whoever is assessing your work that you have *understood* what you have been studying.

From this brief discussion you will have recognized the importance of remembering *to whom* you are writing, and *why*, before you begin to write. Both your style of writing and the content will vary according to your intended reader and what it is you are trying to say. Most of the formal writing you will be expected to do for assignments in the course will require the use of properly formed sentences rather than abbreviated notes. Even if you are very confident about your writing skills, it is worth reading Box 5.1, *Making sense in sentences*, now.

Box 5.1 Making sense in sentences

To begin with, let's look at the first stage involved in turning notes into intelligible text. This means turning notes into proper sentences. Below is a passage of 'intelligible text' that you have already read in this book. Read it through again, at your normal reading speed.

> figure 4.17 shows that some water vapour rises over the oceans and that some is blown inland and moves upwards over land masses as the air and the water vapour it contains rises it cools down you may have experienced this decrease in temperature when climbing a hill or mountain if you have ever walked up ben nevis you will know that even in summer there is ice near the summit also at the base of everest there is sub-tropical vegetation the summit is decidedly less hospitable as the air becomes colder some of the water vapour condenses into water droplets which form a cloud the process is just like the clouds of condensation that form when you exhale warm air from your lungs into a cold atmosphere an effect that is particularly noticeable on cold winter days and nights in a cloud the small droplets join together to make larger droplets and eventually the droplets grow too large to be held in the air any longer and start to fall to earth you are of course familiar with the end product of this process rain

○ What is wrong with this passage about the formation of clouds and rain, as we have reproduced it above?

○ The passage contains no indication of where one sentence ends and the next begins, because there are no full stops and no capital letters. There is no other form of punctuation, either.

○ When you read this passage at your normal speed, how easy was it to make sense of it?

○ You probably found it quite hard, even though the content should have been familiar to you.

This passage illustrates the importance of using properly punctuated sentences so that your writing can be understood easily.

Activity 5.2 Punctuating text

In this activity you will add appropriate punctuation to the unpunctuated passage on the left. The passage is reprinted in the Study File. ◀

From Activity 5.2 you can see how important it is to break up your writing into properly structured sentences so that your readers know what you mean, rather than having to make their own interpretations. Note that as well as being used to signal the start of sentences, capital letters are used for the names of people and places, and anything else that has a unique identity. As you work through this course, it is important to note which scientific terms begin with capital letters and which don't.

Question 5.1 Which of the following words you have met so far in this book should begin with a capital letter, and why?

barrel cactus, desert, celsius scale, sahara desert, oxygen, arctic circle, earth. ◀

Words into sentences

In the preceding discussion we have assumed that you understand how a sentence is constructed, apart from it being a sequence of words beginning with a capital letter, and ending with a full stop. You may do so, either intuitively from your experience of reading what others have written, or because you were taught the rudiments of English grammar during your school career.

To make sense, a sentence must contain at least one *verb*, which is a word describing some sort of action (a word of 'doing'), and something or someone to carry out the action (the *subject* of the verb). Within the context of the water cycle, the simplest possible sentence consists of just two words, a verb and its subject, for example: 'Rain falls.'.

○ What is the verb in this sentence, and what is the subject?

○ 'Falls' is the verb because it describes an action, and 'rain' is the subject because it is the rain that is falling.

The statement constitutes a sentence because it not only contains a subject and a verb, but it is also self-contained. It makes complete sense, devoid of any other words.

○ Suppose we substituted 'falling' for 'falls'. Would the sentence still be self-contained?

○ No, it wouldn't. If you say it aloud, it sounds incomplete.

A verb that ends in '-ing' is incomplete. The technical term for this form of the verb is the *present participle*, but you are not expected to remember this. To complete the sentence you would need to add something else, including another verb, for example: 'Rain *is* falling.'.

○ Consider another very simple sentence, containing a subject 'heat' and a verb 'evaporates': 'The Sun's heat evaporates.'. Is this a self-contained sentence?

○ 'The Sun's heat evaporates' is not a self-contained sentence. We know that this heat is able to cause evaporation, but we need to say *what it is* that the heat is evaporating.

For this sentence to be complete and make sense, the verb must be followed by an *object* indicating someone or something that is having whatever it is done to them. This may be a single word, for example 'water'. 'The Sun's heat evaporates *water*.' Or it may consist of a group of words, such as those shown in italics in this example: 'The Sun's heat evaporates *what is left behind* once the flood waters have drained away.'. Any group of words, such as 'the Sun's heat evaporates' or 'rain falling' that does not form a complete sentence is called a *phrase*.

The use of commas

Most writing contains forms of punctuation other than full stops, most commonly the comma. When you read a sentence aloud, the effect of a comma is to build in a slight pause. This pause helps to break up the sentence so that you can make sense of it more easily. Look at this short passage of text, and notice where the commas are placed:

> Some countries, such as Switzerland, have heavy snowfall which, as it thaws, forms vast, raging, gushing torrents of water that tumble down the steep mountain streams, and which is used to generate hydro-electric power. A water droplet or thawed snowflake might soak into the soil, or fall on pavements and roads, or it may run off directly into a stream or river.

Commas are used in three different ways in this passage.

1   They are used in between lists of two or more *adjectives* (descriptive words): 'vast, raging, gushing'. Note, however, that there is no comma in between the last adjective, 'gushing', and the word that all the adjectives describe, 'torrents'.

2   They occur *in pairs* around the phrases 'such as Switzerland' and 'as it thaws'. In each of these examples, the phrases not only separate a subject from its verb ('countries … have', 'snowfall … forms'), they also describe the subject in some way. 'Such as Switzerland' is an example of 'some countries', and 'as it thaws' describes what happens to 'snowfall'.

3   They are used to break up long lists of items, as in the second sentence where several possible alternative fates for a raindrop or thawed snowflake are described.

Activity 5.3   *Sentences and verbs*

This activity is about identifying verbs and their correct use in sentences. ◀

Activity 5.4 Putting commas into sentences

This activity requires you to add commas to an extract of a student's account of the potato experiment to make it easier to follow. ◄

5.2 The three 'Cs'

Of all the skills involved in studying and learning, that of writing is, perhaps, the most daunting. Even very experienced scientists or authors may find it difficult to put pen to paper (or fingers to keyboard) when they are ready to publish their findings or to write teaching texts, like this book. Why should this be so? To answer this question, consider a mathematics problem of the sort you have already encountered. When you are dealing with this sort of calculation there is usually only a single correct answer. By contrast, there are many ways of putting over what you want to say in writing, and some will be more effective than others. Deciding which way is best can be a source of anxiety. Also, writing *tests your understanding* of a subject; if you haven't understood something properly, it will show up in what you write and no one wants to display ignorance. Fortunately, the challenge of writing also involves thinking fairly deeply about what it is you have to write and this, in turn, helps you to develop a better understanding of the subject. This is why writing assignments is such a valuable aid to learning.

So what makes good scientific writing that is effective in communicating your ideas? Broadly speaking, the answer lies in the three Cs: *conciseness, coherence* and *clarity*.

Conciseness means saying what you want to say in as few words as are feasible. *Coherence* involves making sure that your piece of writing has a logical flow, and hangs together properly; in other words, that you are saying things in an order that will make sense to someone else trying to follow your argument. Conciseness and coherence will both help to ensure *clarity,* but there are other factors, as well, that are equally crucial if you want your writing to be totally clear to those who read it. We shall explore these other factors later in this section.

> Conciseness, coherence and clarity are the key to good scientific writing.

5.2.1 Conciseness

Most writing you will come across, or for which you are responsible, will consist of sentences that are far more complex than those we have used as examples in Box 5.1. Indeed, it would be very tedious to read writing that consisted of sentences each with a very basic construction. However, the longer and more complex your sentence is, the more chance there is that it will be difficult for others to understand. Being concise means saying what you want to say in as few words as possible, without loss of meaning. It is the opposite of a rambling style which is often repetitious, or full of irrelevancies, and so difficult to understand. Consider the following two sentences that are attempting to say the same thing about the process of evaporation.

1 The process of evaporation, when it occurs, is important because not only does it result in water being evaporated into the air where it may condense into water droplets to form clouds which may lead eventually to rain which will fall onto the land surface, but also because it leads to the water evaporated, if it is evaporated from the oceans, being separated from all the dissolved and solid substances.

2 The process of evaporation is important, not only for the cycling of water, but also because the water evaporated from the oceans is separated from all the dissolved and solid substances they contain.

○ Which of the two sentences about evaporation is easier to understand?

○ We are sure that you had no difficulty answering this. The second sentence, which is a shorter and more direct statement, is easier to understand.

Both statements give two reasons why the process of evaporation is important. The first reason is signalled by 'not only', and the second by 'but also'. In the first sentence various aspects of the water cycle are described. These are summarized by the phrase 'the cycling of water' in the second sentence. Because of the extended explanation in the first sentence, by the time you reached 'but also', you had probably forgotten what the first reason was, if not what the whole statement was about. This rambling style also obscures the main point of the sentence which is to explain how water becomes separated from dissolved and solid substances during evaporation. There are also a lot of other redundant (unnecessary) words in the first sentence.

Activity 5.5 *Writing concisely: evaporation*

This activity requires you to cross out redundant words and phrases in sentence 1 above, so that the amended sentence is easier to understand. The sentence is reprinted in the Study File. ◀

5.2.2 Coherence

For a piece of writing to be coherent it must have a logical flow. Imagine that you are following a recipe to make a cake or following a set of instructions to construct a piece of furniture from a D-I-Y store 'flatpack'. The instructions need to be given in the most logical order, otherwise you will end up either taking twice as long to make the product, or with a disaster.

Activity 5.6 *Writing with a logical flow*

This activity requires you to rearrange some sentences so that they describe in a logical order the journey of a glass of water through the human body. ◀

5.2.3 Clarity

Sections 5.2.1 and 5.2.2 show how conciseness and coherence both lead to clarity in your writing. A factor that diminishes clarity is *ambiguity,* which arises when a phrase or sentence has more than one meaning. In Box 5.1 you saw how the lack of proper sentence construction is one source of ambiguity.

Sometimes it is the way in which words are ordered in a sentence that leads to ambiguity. Consider this sentence: 'The bottle of frozen milk on the doorstep on a winter's morning which is mostly composed of water expands when it freezes.'

○ According to this sentence, what is mostly composed of water?

○ Common sense tells you it must be the milk. However, the way the sentence is written implies that it could be the doorstep or the winter's morning, instead.

How could the words be reordered so that the sentence is not ambiguous? You could place the phrase 'which is mostly composed of water' directly after the word it describes so that the sentence reads: 'The bottle of frozen milk, which is mostly

I'VE DISCUSSED THE PLAN FOR RESTOCKING THE LARDER WITH THE STAFF IN MY KITCHEN

composed of water, on the doorstep on a winter's morning expands when it freezes.' The sentence is now rather clumsy and it is still ambiguous because it is the frozen milk that expands, not the bottle. To make it easier to follow, a little more shuffling around is required and a slight change in wording: 'Milk, which is mostly composed of water, expands when it freezes in the bottle on the doorstep on a winter's morning.'. The milk is now followed by the phrase which describes it, and the verbs 'expands' and 'freezes', which are related processes, are almost next to each other. It is also clear, now, that it is the milk, and not the bottle, which expands.

The golden rule when writing is: *place the words most closely related to each other as near to each other as possible.* If you observe this simple rule, you will avoid at least some sources of ambiguity.

5.3   Sentences into paragraphs

You will have noticed when reading this book, or any book, magazine or newspaper article, that the printed text is not continuous down the page. It is broken up into discrete chunks called *paragraphs*. Sometimes one paragraph is separated from the next by a gap, a line where no text is printed. An alternative format involves beginning each new paragraph by indenting the first line a little way. Which of these methods is used depends upon an editor's or publisher's preference.

Activity 5.7   The importance of paragraphs

This activity asks you to consider how paragraphs have been used to break up the text in Section 5.1. ◄

The comments on Activity 5.7 show the importance of paragraphs as signals, or visual cues, to the reader that there is about to be a change in the discussion. They also make the printed page much easier to read. You can imagine how daunting it would be for your study of science if you were faced with whole sections of this book as continuous text. Your tutor-counsellor will feel equally daunted by your assignments if they are not properly structured in paragraphs to break up the subject matter of your answers.

When you begin your first piece of assessed writing as part of this course, you will probably be more concerned to 'get it all down' than to worry about your writing style. This doesn't matter, provided you are prepared to go back over what you have written with a critical eye, to make sure it is structured correctly and contains no unnecessary words and phrases.

GOT A LITTLE CARRIED AWAY, DIDN'T WE?

5.4   Concluding comments

In this section, we have had time and space to discuss only the most essential elements of good writing as an aid to communicating science. However, before moving on to the next stage in our exploration of the necessity of water for life, it is important that we point out the differences between the writing that you will find in this course, and that in most scientific accounts. By 'scientific accounts' we mean reports of experiments, articles written by scientists in scientific journals, and the answers to assignments that you will write.

We hope that both types of writing (these books and scientific accounts) will represent good writing. However, the former are written to take the place of the sort of dialogue that would occur face-to-face between you and your tutor in a conventional teaching situation. Therefore their style is much more 'chatty' and informal than a scientific account, in which the author aims to present information such as observations, experimental procedures and results, and hypotheses in as concise a manner as is reasonable.

Activity 5.8 Turning key points into sentences and paragraphs

In this activity you will write some sentences and paragraphs about cacti and camels, based on key points identified from the text. ◀

5.5 Summary of Section 5

Good writing in science requires you to:

- remember to whom you are writing, and why, before you begin to write;
- use completed sentences that contain a verb with a subject and, where appropriate, an object;
- use commas between adjectives (in lists of two or more), to separate items in a list, and around phrases that separate a verb from its subject or object;
- keep your writing concise by avoiding unnecessary repetition and redundant words;
- make sure that what you write has a logical flow so that it is coherent;
- maintain clarity in your writing, avoiding ambiguities by placing the words most closely related to each other as near to each other as possible;
- use a new paragraph for each new subject and to break up the text.

Activity 5.1 Planning your study (continued)

Before leaving Section 5, check your log of study time and compare it with your work plan. Now would be a good time to adjust your plans for studying Sections 6 and 7 if necessary. ◀

6 Water, society and the environment

The ways in which human activities interact with the water cycle can have devastating consequences for all forms of life. Much of Section 6 will be dedicated to exploring the ways in which we exploit the water that is available for our use. You will be introduced to the use of powers of ten, which are a convenient way of expressing both very large and very small numbers. Finally, you will be transported to a faraway (fictional) planet that is almost devoid of surface water. In other words, it is a desert. The author, Frank Herbert, set his novel *Dune* on this planet. You will be given an extract from *Dune*, describing how fictional human beings have adapted to life in such inhospitable conditions, and you will be asked to explain in your own words the science that lies behind the extract.

As you study this section you will be drawing on facts and concepts that you have met in earlier sections. You will be gratified at the amount of science that you have already learned — even at this early stage in the course — and how many skills you have developed along the way.

Activity 6.1 Listing key points

Summarizing is a very important activity because it not only provides you with a written record of the key points that you have noted as you have been studying, but it also helps to reinforce your learning. We would like you to practise summarizing as you study Section 6. ◄

6.1 'Water, water, everywhere ...'

When astronauts first ventured to the Moon in the late 1960s, they were captivated by a vision of the Earth in colour as it had never been seen before (Figure 6.1). It is not surprising that after pictures like this were published, the Earth became known as the 'blue planet'.

Figure 6.1 A view of the Earth from space. The brown areas are North and South America, the blue areas are the oceans and the white areas are cloud.

It is astonishing just how much of the Earth's surface is covered by water. The oceans occupy about 71% of the Earth's surface. Altogether, the total volume of water on the

Earth, including the oceans, lakes, rivers and what is stored in rocks underground, is estimated to be roughly 1 460 000 000 000 000 000 000 (1 460 billion billion) litres.

● Can you recall what the average daily intake of water is for a person in the UK (from food as well as drinks)?

○ It's around 2.5 litres (see Table 4.2 in Section 4.4.3).

Even allowing 5 litres per person to ensure the most basic standard of domestic use (i.e. the minimum for cooking and washing), in addition to what we take into our bodies, it would be reasonable to imagine that there is enough water around to sustain not only the Earth's 6 000 000 000 (6 billion) human inhabitants, but all the other species of animals and plants as well — with an awful lot to spare.

However, we frequently receive news bulletins that illustrate the appalling consequences of droughts in some parts of our world. Even in Britain we sometimes suffer water shortages as, for example, during the summer of 1995. Even so, we are inclined to grumble about the frequent rainfall (whenever we are not grumbling about the droughts!). It seems that the planet is well endowed with life-giving water but, from a human perspective, it is often in the wrong place, in the wrong form (for example, seawater is plentiful in coastal towns but fresh drinking water could be in short supply), or available at the wrong time.

6.1.1 The Earth's store of water

To find out why we can talk about water shortages and droughts on a planet endowed with 1 460 000 000 000 000 000 000 litres of water, we have to look at where our water occurs. But first we will make the numbers a bit more manageable by introducing a larger unit to measure the volumes. The unit most commonly used for this purpose is the cubic kilometre, abbreviated to km^3, which is the volume of a cube with sides 1 km long. One cubic kilometre is equivalent to 1 000 000 000 000 litres, or a million million litres, and we can demonstrate this as follows.

We want to know how many litres (each of which is equivalent to a 10 cm cube, introduced in Box 4.2) can be stacked up in a 1 km cube. There are 10 lots of 10 centimetres in one metre (since 10×10 cm = 100 cm = 1 m), and there are 1 000 metres in 1 kilometre, and so there are $10 \times 1 000$ lots, or 10 000 lots, of 10 centimetres in 1 kilometre. This means that 10 000 one litre cubes could be placed side by side along one edge of a one kilometre cube. So the total number of one litre cubes that could be stacked within a one kilometre cube is $10 000 \times 10 000 \times 10 000$, which is 1 000 000 000 000. The relationship between litres and km^3, m^3 and cm^3 is summarized in the margin.

A cubic kilometre is 1 000 000 000 000 times *larger* than a litre, so the number of cubic kilometres of water on the Earth is 1 000 000 000 000 times *smaller* than the number of litres. This means that the number of cubic kilometres of water on Earth is

$$\frac{1\,460\,000\,000\,\cancel{000}\,\cancel{000}\,\cancel{000}\,\cancel{000}}{1\,\cancel{000}\,\cancel{000}\,\cancel{000}\,\cancel{000}} = 1\,460\,000\,000$$

Notice how 12 zeros have been cancelled out. (Look back to Box 2.4 if you need reminding how to do this.) This makes the number representing the total water volume a bit more manageable, and this volume is shown as the bottom line in Table 6.1, together with the volumes (in km^3) stored in each of the Earth's various natural reservoirs. (Don't confuse this use of the term 'reservoir' with the reservoirs that are

Units of volume

$1\ km^3 = 1\ 000\ 000\ 000\ 000$ litres

$1\ m^3 = 1\ 000$ litres

$1\ cm^3 = 1/1\ 000$ litre
so $1\ 000\ cm^3 = 1$ litre

built to store water for human use.) The volumes listed in Table 6.1 for ice and snow and for the atmosphere are the volumes of liquid water that would be produced by melting the solid ice and snow and by condensing the water vapour from the atmosphere. It is important to note that all of the volumes shown in Table 6.1 are estimates; clearly no one has been able to measure the volume of water in the oceans accurately.

Table 6.1   Estimates of volumes of water stored in natural reservoirs on the Earth.

Reservoir	Volume/km³	Volume/% total water
oceans	1 400 000 000	96
ice and snow	43 000 000	
underground water	15 000 000	1.0
lakes and rivers	360 000	0.025
atmosphere	15 000	0.001
plants and animals	2 000	0.000 14
total	1 460 000 000*	100*

*The numbers in the middle column of the table actually add up to 1 458 377 000, but we have rounded this to 1 460 000 000 to reflect the limited accuracy of the larger numbers. For the same reason, when you have filled the gap in the third column (Question 6.1), you will find that the numbers do not add to exactly 100. We will discuss the number of digits that are appropriate in different circumstances in later blocks.

Even though we have got rid of 12 zeros by expressing the volumes in km³ rather than litres, the numbers in the middle column of Table 6.1 are still too large to be handled easily. There are still too many zeros around. It is much easier to work with percentages of the total water volume in the Earth's natural reservoirs, and these are displayed in the right-hand column of the table. You can see that about 96% of the water is stored in the oceans, which means that there is only a small percentage available for our use on the land. To put it another way, if all the Earth's water was represented by the contents of a 4.5 litre (1 gallon) can, all but the contents of a teacup would be seawater.

Question 6.1   There is a gap in the right-hand column of Table 6.1. Calculate the proportion of water that is stored in ice and snow as a percentage of the total volume of water stored on Earth, and enter your answer in the table.

(*Hint*   To do this, first write down the proportion as a fraction. Because the numbers involved are too large to enter in a calculator (try entering 1 460 000 000 if you like), you will then need to reduce the fraction to an equivalent fraction with smaller numbers on the top and the bottom by cancelling out some zeros. Then use your calculator to work out the required percentage.) ◄

Percentages are one way to avoid having to work with cumbersome numbers like those in Table 6.1, but an alternative is to use a mathematical notation for expressing the numbers in a more convenient form, which disposes of all the zeros. This method is called '**powers of ten**' and is based on the observation that every time we multiply a number by 10, we add a zero to the end of the number. This is explained in Box 6.1, *Going up: powers of ten for large numbers, and scientific notation.*

Box 6.1 Going up: powers of ten for large numbers, and scientific notation

Let's go back to our value for the total volume of water stored on the Earth: $1\,460\,000\,000\,km^3$.

When dealing with large numbers like one thousand four hundred and sixty million ($1\,460\,000\,000$), it becomes tedious to write out the number in words or to keep writing out all of the zeros. Worse still, it is very easy to lose some of the zeros or add extra ones by mistake. Fortunately, we can refer to large numbers without having to write out all of the zeros. The powers of ten notation is less prone to errors and tedium because it removes the zeros. We will introduce the powers of ten notation with some numbers more manageable than $1\,460\,000\,000$, though.

One thousand is normally written as $1\,000$. There are three zeros, so in the powers of ten notation this would be written as 10^3. The number 3 in 10^3 is called the **power**, and the complete number is spoken as 'ten to the power 3'. Note that the power is printed as a superscript. Let's explain the use of this notation.

One thousand is ten times ten times ten:

$10 \times 10 \times 10 = 1\,000$

Three tens have been multiplied together to give one thousand. We can show this by writing down the ten and then indicating the number of tens that have been multiplied together with a superscript — the power. In the case of one thousand, the power is 3, so we write 10^3.

⬤ How do you think you would write 100 in powers of ten?

◯ Two tens are multiplied together to give one hundred ($10 \times 10 = 100$) so the superscript after the 10 must be 2. That's 10^2.

When expressing 100 and $1\,000$ in powers of ten, there are no great savings on writing zeros, but what about one million ($1\,000\,000$)? One million is the product of multiplying together six tens:

$10 \times 10 \times 10 \times 10 \times 10 \times 10 = 1\,000\,000$

so it is written as 10^6. Now you begin to see the benefit of the powers of ten notation.

You may remember that when we were discussing areas and volumes (Box 4.2), we introduced the units m^2 (square metres) and m^3 (cubic metres). The superscripts used there — the 2 and the 3 — are powers too, but they are powers of m rather than powers of ten. So m^2 means $m \times m$, and m^3 means $m \times m \times m$. We shall come back to powers of things, besides ten, later in this book.

One thousand is often written not just as 10^3 but as 1×10^3. Spoken aloud, this would be expressed, 'one times ten to the power three'. Likewise one million is either 1×10^6 or simply 10^6. Now we can give two alternative explanations that may help you to get to grips with powers of ten. The power of ten shows how many times 1 has been multiplied by 10. Taking 1×10^3 as an example, $1\,000$ is seen to be $1 \times 10 \times 10 \times 10$. In a second view, the power of ten shows how many places the decimal point has to move to the right to give the actual number. If we write 1 as 1.0 to remind ourselves where the decimal point is, then one move to the right would turn 1.0 into 10.0, a second move would give 100.0 and a third move would give $1\,000.0$, that is, one thousand.

$$1 . \overset{\frown\frown}{0\ 0}\ 0\ 0$$

You do not have to recall both of these ways of understanding powers of ten; just use the one that suits you best, or develop your own way of fixing the idea in your armoury of mathematical techniques.

Let's go back to the total amount of water on the Earth. Using the powers of ten notation, $1\,460\,000\,000$ could be written as 1.46×10^9. A significant saving on zeros! The complete number would be spoken as 'one point four six times ten to the power 9'. The power of 9 tells us how many times 1.46 has been multiplied by 10 to give the final number of $1\,460\,000\,000$. It is nine times. That is, our number is comprised of:

$1.46 \times 10 \times 10 \times 10 \times 10 \times 10 \times 10 \times 10 \times 10 \times 10$

To see clearly that this expression is still one thousand four hundred and sixty million, it helps to begin with 1.46 and work our way to the number we want by multiplying each time by ten.

1.46			
1.46×10	=	14.6	= 1.46×10^1
$1.46 \times 10 \times 10$	=	146	= 1.46×10^2
$1.46 \times 10 \times 10 \times 10$	=	$1\,460$	= 1.46×10^3

If we carry on doing this, we end up with:

$1.46 \times 10 \times 10 \times 10 \times 10 \times 10 \times 10 \times 10 \times 10 \times 10$

$= 1\,460\,000\,000 = 1.46 \times 10^9$

Alternatively you can think of each increase by one in the power of ten as moving the decimal point one place to the right. That is, if you multiply 1.46 by 10 the decimal point moves one place to the right, giving 14.6.

1 . 4 6

Likewise, to multiply 1.46 by one thousand, the decimal point moves three places to the right, giving 1 460.0.

In the powers of ten notation, this is written 1.46×10^3.

1 . 4 6 0 0

There is a convention called **scientific notation** that is used when writing a number with a power of ten. Scientific notation requires the number accompanying the power of ten to be less than 10 but equal to or greater than 1. Let's take the example of one million. It could be correctly expressed as 1×10^6, 10×10^5, 100×10^4, $1\,000 \times 10^3$, and so on, or even as 0.1×10^7, but only the first of these obeys the convention of scientific notation and this is the one that should be used. As a second example, it is quite correct mathematically to write 85 000 as 85×10^3, or 0.85×10^5, but correct scientific notation would demand 8.5×10^4.

> Scientific notation requires the number accompanying the power of ten to be less than 10 but equal to or greater than 1.

In summary, a power of ten indicates how many times a number has to be multiplied by 10 to make the final number. A few examples are given below, along with their names.

10^1	=	10	ten
10^2	=	100	one hundred
10^3	=	1 000	one thousand
10^6	=	1 000 000	one million
10^9	=	1 000 000 000	one billion
10^{12}	=	1 000 000 000 000	one million million

Question 6.2   Express the following numbers in scientific notation: (a) 100 000 000; (b) 400 000 000 000; (c) 35 000; (d) 95×10^5; (e) 0.51×10^3. ◀

Question 6.3   Write out in full the numbers corresponding to: (a) 7.3×10^4; (b) 3.6×10^6; (c) 4.44×10^5; (d) 6.05×10^3. ◀

Question 6.4   There are said to be 1 460 000 000 000 000 000 000 litres of water stored on Earth. Express this number in a more concise form that obeys the convention of scientific notation. ◀

Powers of ten with calculators and computers

Powers of ten can be entered and displayed in scientific calculators, and you need to be familiar with how this is done. You may already have seen how powers of ten are displayed on your own calculator, but in case you haven't, key in the following calculation:

6 0 0 0 0 0 × 6 0 0 0 0 0 =

The display will show something like 3.6 ^{11} or 3.6 11. This means 3.6×10^{11}, which is the same as 360 000 000 000. The two numerals (or digits) at the right of the display are the power of ten, and these are usually displayed in a smaller size than the other numerals. *Note that the ten is not displayed.* Thus 3.234 ^{04} means 3.234×10^4, and 5.09 ^{12} means 5.09×10^{12}.

Entering powers of ten in a calculator is straightforward — once you have discovered how to do it! Your calculator will have a special key for this purpose, which may be labelled EE, E or EXP (Figure 2.5). We shall use EE here. So to enter 5.09×10^{12} you would key in

5 . 0 9 and then EE and then 1 2

Try doing this with your calculator, and observe the display after each key press. The final display should be 5.09 ^{12}. What you must remember when entering powers of ten is that *you don't key in the multiplication sign or the 10.* If you key in 5 . 0 9 and then × 1 0 and then EE and then 1 2 the display will show 5.09 ^{13}, which is 5.09×10^{13}, because the calculator interprets what you keyed as $5.09 \times 10 \times 10^{12}$. If you simply want to enter 10^{12}, then you have to enter 1 EE 1 2, which the calculator interprets as 1×10^{12}. Again, try this on your calculator.

You won't be required to do calculations using powers of ten in this block, but check that you can enter the following numbers in your calculator: 4.293×10^{21} (displayed as 4.293 ^{21}); 8.21×10^7 (8.21 ^{07}); 3.14×10^{13} (3.14 ^{13}).

Computers and programmable calculators often use a different way of entering and displaying powers of ten. For example, 5.09×10^{12} would be entered and displayed as 5.09E12. You can think of the E standing for the $\times 10$, with the 12 being the power that is attached to the 10.

⬤ How would 3.478×10^3 be displayed on a scientific calculator and on a computer?

◯ It would appear as 3.478 ^{03} on a calculator, and 3.478E3 on a computer.

Let's present the numbers in Table 6.1 in a different way. In Figure 6.2 we have given them more visual interest by displaying them in a diagram that shows the locations of the reservoirs as well. The amounts of water stored in the various natural reservoirs are shown in the boxes.

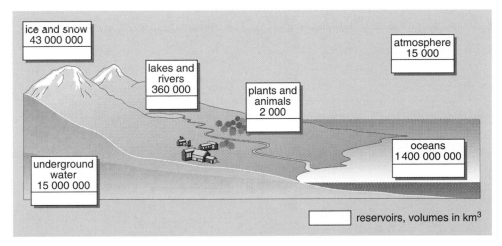

Figure 6.2 The amounts of water, in km^3, stored within natural reservoirs on the Earth.

Question 6.5 You will see that beneath each number quoted on Figure 6.2, there is a space. Convert each number into correct scientific notation, and write your answers in the appropriate spaces. ◀

6.1.2 The 'salt' in seawater

The difficulty we face by having so much of the Earth's water locked up in the oceans is summed up poetically by Coleridge's 'Ancient Mariner', becalmed on board ship in the doldrums, beneath a blazing Sun.

> Water, water, everywhere,
> And all the boards did shrink;
> Water, water, everywhere,
> Nor any drop to drink.

> (Samuel Taylor Coleridge, *The Rime of the Ancient Mariner*, 1797–1798)

With so much Pacific Ocean around them, and dying of thirst, why didn't the ship's crew just lower a bucket and bring up some seawater to drink? As you are aware, there is a very important difference between seawater and fresh water. Seawater contains various salts. The most abundant of these salts is known as sodium chloride, the most common constituent of table salt. Other salts contain calcium and magnesium. If you were to put 100 g of seawater in a pan and boil it, you would find about 3.5 g of the different salts left behind as a residue after all the water had evaporated. Although we require some salts in our diet, there is only a certain amount that we can tolerate. The excess beyond this is removed by our bodies.

○ How would these excess salts be removed from our bodies? (Think back to Section 4.4.3, A drink of water.)

○ Some salts may be lost in sweat, but most of the excess is removed by the kidneys and excreted in urine.

The problem for the kidneys is that in order to remove the salts, they need water. The more salts, the more water they require. So after drinking seawater the 'Ancient Mariner' crew would have been even more thirsty, because of the need to remove the excess salts. The problem is compounded by the fact that one of the constituents of the salts in seawater actually irritates the last section of the large intestine called the rectum (see Figure 4.16c). This causes diarrhoea, with a further loss of water. The end result would be that the crew members would be thirstier than before.

It is possible to convert seawater into fresh water by a process called desalination (which means, literally, salt-removal). The easiest and cheapest way to do this is to use the natural energy of the Sun to evaporate seawater, but this is a slow process. Other methods of desalination use different energy sources — oil, for example. Either way, desalination is a costly business and so is generally used only in those countries wealthy enough to afford it (e.g. countries in the Arabian Peninsula, Iran and the United States — in Arizona and California), and only where there is no other source of fresh water. The salt residue left over from the evaporation of seawater may be used as a commercial source for the brands of table salt that are sold as 'sea salt'. One such brand boasts on its label: 'Obtained from the Mediterranean Sea, naturally evaporated by the hot sun'.

There have even been proposals to tow icebergs, which contain a large amount of frozen fresh water, from the Arctic and Antarctic Oceans to areas where the fresh water is needed. These icebergs are formed where the Antarctic ice sheet and Arctic Greenland glaciers, both fed by snowfall, meet the sea. While this scheme is theoretically possible, it is beset with all sorts of problems. Not the least of these is how to get an iceberg to its destination without most of it melting on the way.

6.1.3 The study of a raindrop

Notwithstanding desalination schemes, by far and away the majority of our usable water is derived from the 1.1×10^5 km^3 that falls over the land surface each year as rain, snow, sleet or hail. The collective term for all of these sources of water is **precipitation**. You have already discovered how rain is formed as part of the water cycle (Section 4.5). At this point we consider in more detail the size of the drops of water that make up clouds or rain.

The typical distance across a water droplet in a cloud is one hundred-thousandth of a metre, that is, $\frac{1}{100\,000}$ m or 0.000 01 m. This corresponds to $\frac{1}{100}$ mm or 0.01 mm, and is very small. Imagine dividing the gap between adjacent millimetre marks on a ruler into a hundred parts! Many of these droplets coalesce to give a raindrop that has a breadth of about two-thousandths of a metre, ($\frac{2}{1000}$ m, 0.002 m or 2 mm). Even these drops are small, but clearly they are water.

It is interesting to contemplate whether there is such a thing as a smallest particle that is still recognizably water and from which all larger volumes of water are made. In other words, if we start with a raindrop and keep halving its volume, does there come a point when a further reduction gives us something that ceases to be water? It is often useful in science, when dealing with complex ideas, to think of an *analogy*. One analogy for this 'halving' of a drop of water is the defining of a single living cow starting from a small herd of eight cows. If we halve the herd, we get four cows. Repeating the process gives two cows and repeating again gives us one living cow. If this remaining cow were halved, we would all agree that what remains is certainly not a living, whole cow. We would have destroyed the cow. We can conclude that one whole living cow is the smallest item from which herds of any size can be composed. Unfortunately, once a drop of water is halved several times, it becomes extremely small. It is a process that we cannot see with our own eyes — or even with a conventional microscope.

In principle, a typical raindrop — say, 2 mm across — could be halved in volume 67 times before a single particle that is still recognizably water emerges from the crowd. The 68th division by two, like the halving of a single cow, would destroy the water. This smallest particle that is still water is called a water molecule and its dimensions are almost inconceivably small. Molecules are the basic particles of many solids, liquids and gases that you will meet as you study the course.

Because the shape of a water molecule is not regular, its size is not easy to describe. However, if its shape were likened to a tiny sphere, it would be about 0.000 000 000 2 m across. It is difficult to comprehend a number this small, but you can probably imagine why it is impossible to perform the halving experiment with a molecule. Roughly 10^{20} of these molecules would be needed to make a single raindrop.

So, how many water molecules are there in a full glass of water, your body or an ocean? The numbers involved are unimaginably large. Perhaps some appreciation of the scale can be gained by noting that if every human being on the planet were to gather round a beaker containing 100 ml (millilitres) of water, and each person were to count a share of the water molecules in it at the rate of one molecule per second, it would take more than ten million years to count the total number of molecules in the beaker. We shall leave the proof of the existence of molecules and the details of their amazing sub-microscopic world until later in the course.

As when writing very large numbers, there is an inherent danger in writing out very small numbers like 0.000 000 000 2. Once again, the zeros are the problem. There are just too many of them! However, there is a notation that minimizes the risk of making mistakes when working with such numbers. As before, it relies on the powers of ten idea to get rid of many of the zeros, and it's explained in Box 6.2, *Going down: powers of ten for small numbers.*

Box 6.2 Going down: powers of ten for small numbers

In Box 6.1 you saw that the powers of ten notation provides a concise method of expressing very large numbers and reduces the chances of errors when, otherwise, many zeros would have to be written out. Let's see how the powers of ten notation can be extended to cover small numbers, such as 0.000 000 000 2 m.

Write down the next two numbers in each of the following two sequences.

$$10\,000 \quad 1\,000 \quad 100 \quad \dots\dots\dots \quad \dots\dots\dots$$

$$1 \times 10^4 \quad 1 \times 10^3 \quad 1 \times 10^2 \quad \dots\dots\dots \quad \dots\dots\dots$$

In the first sequence, each successive number is *divided* by 10 (i.e. had one zero taken off the end) so the number that follows 100 is $\frac{100}{10} = 10$. The next number in that sequence must result from another division by 10. That is, we must divide 10 by 10 and $\frac{10}{10} = 1$. Therefore, the second answer is 1. In the second sequence of numbers, each successive number has 1 *subtracted* from its power, so the first answer is 1×10^1 because $2 - 1 = 1$. For the second answer, we must subtract 1 from the power 1. Because $1 - 1 = 0$, the next answer is 1×10^0.

In fact, both sequences are the same because 10 000 is 1×10^4, 1 000 is 1×10^3, 100 is 1×10^2, and 10 is 1×10^1. The implication is that $1 = 1 \times 10^0$ and hence $10^0 = 1$. This makes perfectly good sense if you recall that, in the second sequence given above, the power is the number of times that 1 is multiplied by ten (e.g. $10^2 = 1 \times 10 \times 10$). For 1×10^0, 1 is multiplied by 10 no times at all, leaving it as 1.

Why stop at 1 or 10^0? Using the same rules, write down the next number in each of these sequences.

$$100 \quad 10 \quad 1 \quad \dots\dots\dots$$

$$1 \times 10^2 \quad 1 \times 10^1 \quad 1 \times 10^0 \quad \dots\dots\dots$$

In the first sequence, dividing 1 by 10 gives $\frac{1}{10}$ or 0.1 as the next number. In this box, we're keeping to decimals, so the answer we want is 0.1. But what about the second sequence? The answer is more straightforward than it may seem. We continue to subtract 1 from the powers of ten so that the next number in the sequence has a negative power of ten (1×10^{-1}) because $0 - 1 = -1$. Remembering that the two sequences are equivalent, it seems that $1 \times 10^{-1} = 0.1$. This is exactly right! We could equally write $10^{-1} = 0.1$.

Just as a positive power of ten denotes how many times a number is *multiplied* by 10, so a negative power of ten denotes how many times a number is *divided* by 10. For 10^{-1}, we must divide 1 by 10 just once and we end up with 0.1.

⬤ What is the meaning of 10^{-2}?

◯ Because the power is now -2, we must divide 1 by 10 *twice*. That is, $1 \div 10 \div 10 = 0.01$.

Another way to think about powers of ten for very small numbers involves shifting the decimal point. A negative power of ten denotes the number of places that the decimal point moves to the left. For example, think of 1×10^{-2}, which we will write as 1.0×10^{-2} to remind us of the position of the decimal point. Starting with the number 1.0, the power of -2 requires us to move the decimal point 2 places to the left. One place to the left gives 0.1 and two places 0.01.

$$0 \,\, 0 \,\, 1 \,.\, 0$$

We, therefore, have $10^{-2} = 0.01$.

Let's try an example. Suppose a raindrop has a breadth of about 0.002 m. This distance could be given in scientific notation as 2×10^{-3} m. This is clear from the following series.

Start with: 2

Divide by ten: $2 \div 10 = 0.2 = 2.0 \times 10^{-1}$

Divide by ten again: $2 \div 10 \div 10 = 0.02 = 2.0 \times 10^{-2}$

And again: $2 \div 10 \div 10 \div 10 = 0.002 = 2.0 \times 10^{-3}$

Alternatively, in considering the meaning of 'two times ten to the power minus three,' you may wish to start with the number 2.0 and move the decimal point three places to the left to give 0.002.

You have already met the idea of 'moving the decimal point'. In Box 6.1 on expressing large numbers as powers of ten, you learned that a positive power of ten denotes the number of places that the decimal point moves to the *right*. You have now found that a negative power of ten denotes the number of places that the decimal point moves to the *left*.

You have seen that a negative power of ten tells you how many times you need to divide by ten, so that

$$0.001 = 10^{-3} = 1 \div 10 \div 10 \div 10 = \frac{1}{1000}$$

But, of course, $1\,000 = 10^3$, and so

$$0.001 = 10^{-3} = \frac{1}{1000} = \frac{1}{10^3}, \text{ and so } 10^{-3} = \frac{1}{10^3}$$

This relationship between positive and negative powers of ten is quite general, so

$$10^{-6} = \frac{1}{10^6}, \; 10^{-8} = \frac{1}{10^8}, \; 10^{-13} = \frac{1}{10^{13}}, \text{ and so on.}$$

You should recall that in Box 6.1 you were introduced to scientific notation. This convention requires that, when writing large numbers, the power of ten should be accompanied by a number that is equal to or greater than 1 but less than 10. The same convention is used when dealing with small numbers and hence negative powers of ten. This is why 0.002 m, the breadth of the raindrop, is given in scientific notation as 2×10^{-3} m, and not as 0.2×10^{-2} m or 20×10^{-4} m.

In Box 6.1 we showed you how to enter positive powers of ten in a scientific calculator. Entering negative powers of ten is a bit more tricky, because you have to put in the minus sign. You do this using the $\boxed{+/-}$ key (Figure 2.5), which changes the sign of a number. Try entering 5.09×10^{-12}, by pressing the following keys, watching how the numbers appear in the display as you do so:

$\boxed{5}\boxed{.}\boxed{0}\boxed{9} \; \boxed{EE} \; \boxed{1}\boxed{2} \; \boxed{+/-}$

Notice that as you press the $\boxed{+/-}$ key, a minus sign appears in front of the 12 in the display, meaning that the power has become −12, 'minus twelve'. If you press the $\boxed{+/-}$ key again, the minus sign disappears, meaning that the power has become +12 (although the + sign is not displayed). Thus in a scientific calculator 5.09×10^{12} is displayed as 5.09 12, and 5.09×10^{-12} is displayed as 5.09 −12. On a computer or a programmable calculator, these numbers would usually appear as 5.09E12 and 5.09E−12, respectively.

One final point about powers of ten. It is correct to say 'ten to the power minus three' for 10^{-3}, but most people take a slight short-cut and refer to it as 'ten to the minus three'. This means exactly the same thing. It is the result of the same desire for brevity that lies behind the spoken 'don't' in place of 'do not'. Here are two further examples. It is very common to speak of 3.4×10^{-5} as 'three point four times ten to the minus five', and 2.0×10^4 as 'two point nought times ten to the four'.

In summary, a negative power of ten indicates how many times a number has been divided by 10 to make the final number. A few examples follow.

10^1	=			10
10^0	=			1
10^{-1}	=	$\frac{1}{10}$	=	0.1
10^{-2}	=	$\frac{1}{100}$	=	0.01
10^{-3}	=	$\frac{1}{1000}$	=	0.001
10^{-6}	=	$\frac{1}{1\,000\,000}$	=	0.000 001
10^{-9}	=	$\frac{1}{1\,000\,000\,000}$	=	0.000 000 001
10^{-12}	=	$\frac{1}{1\,000\,000\,000\,000}$	=	0.000 000 000 001

Note, however, that 10^1, 10^0 and 10^{-1} are rarely used in scientific writing; it is usual to write 10, 1 and 0.1 instead.

Question 6.6 Express the following measurements in scientific notation:

(a) a water molecule, about 0.000 000 000 25 m across;

(b) an average-sized sand grain on a gently sloping beach, about 0.000 25 m across;

(c) the size of one particle of clay, the main constituent of mud, about 1/1 000 000 m across;

(d) the average size of a hailstone, 0.003 5 m across. ◀

Question 6.7 Write out in full the decimal numbers corresponding to:

(a) 7.3×10^{-4};

(b) 2.9×10^{-7}. ◀

Question 6.8 Use powers of ten notation to answer the following questions:

(a) How many millimetres are there in one kilometre?

(b) How many kilometres is one millimetre equal to?

(c) How many litres are there in one cubic kilometre? ◀

Activity 6.1   Listing key points (continued)

Before you move on, you should tackle Stage 2 of this activity for Section 6.1. ◀

Activity 5.1   Planning your study (continued)

Before leaving Section 6.1, check your log of study time and compare it with your work plan. Now would be a good time to adjust your plans, if necessary, for studying the rest of Section 6. ◀

6.2   The need for water

About 1.1×10^5 km³ of water, in the various forms of precipitation, falls globally on the land surface each year but the majority of this evaporates back to the atmosphere. Only about 4×10^4 km³, or about 36%, of the total precipitation runs off into lakes and rivers or seeps into underground reservoirs. However, the amount of this water that we are able to exploit in practice, for use domestically or for industry and irrigation, is estimated to be no more than about 1.4×10^4 km³, just under 13% of the annual precipitation, or about 0.001% of the Earth's total water.

This may not seem like very much, but, shared out among the world's human population, it is still far more than is needed to ensure the basic survival and minimum domestic needs of everyone, as well as leaving plenty over to sustain the other animals and plants with which we share the Earth.

The minimum water intake needed for survival varies for people in different countries, not least because of the sort of climate they live in. Earlier we reminded you that the average person in the UK has a daily water intake of about 2.5 litres.

⬤ Do you think this water intake would be enough to sustain someone living in Nigeria, during April when the average temperature is about 30 °C? If not, why not?

◯ No, it wouldn't. A much higher water intake would be needed to balance the amount likely to be lost due to sweating at such high temperatures.

Depending upon how hot it is, and how much physical work someone has to undertake, it is possible for their daily water requirement to rise to as much as 11 or 12 litres. Without adequate water intake, dehydration occurs very rapidly. With loss of water equal to 5% body mass, you would feel incredibly thirsty, and with 10% loss, you would become very ill.

As humans, however, we depend upon water for rather more than drinking. Our perception of *personal* need is likely to be far greater when water is freely available 'on tap' (Figures 6.3a and b) than when water must be carried from the well or river to the house, and the washing carried to the river (Figure 6.3c).

Not surprisingly, the daily consumption of water for domestic use is very much greater per person in the developed areas of the world, such as Europe and North America, than in developing areas of Africa and Asia. In Question 2.6 you used the information in Table 2.1 to calculate that the domestic use of water in the UK was 136 litres per person per day. Contrast that figure with an estimate made by the charity WaterAid that the average domestic use in developing countries is about 10 litres per person per day.

Figure 6.3 Contrasting uses of water in developed and developing areas of the world.

(a)

(b)

(c)

Question 6.9 (a) What is the domestic consumption per person per day in developing countries as a percentage of that in the UK? Give your answer to one decimal place.

(b) The total daily consumption per person in the UK is 604 litres. (You worked this out in Question 2.6.) What is the domestic consumption as a *percentage* of the total consumption of water per person per day in the UK? Give your answer to one decimal place. ◄

In contrast with the answer to Question 6.9b, world-wide water for domestic use accounts for only 8% of *total* world water usage. Far more demanding are the needs of industry (23%) and irrigation for crop production (69%), with the developed nations using more for industry, and the developing nations using more for agriculture. For example, it takes on average 8 litres of water to produce 1 litre (2.2 pints) of beer, 1 000 litres to grow 1 kg of wheat, and 30 000 litres to manufacture an average-sized car.

Activity 6.1 Listing key points (continued)

Before you move on, remember to look back at your notes and highlighting in Section 6.2, and produce a list of the main points. Compare your list with the one in the comments on this activity before studying Section 6.3. ◄

Figure 6.4 Foaming effluent on a polluted stream near Zabrze, Poland, in an area suffering some of the worst industrial pollution found anywhere in the world.

6.3 'Sweet Thames run softly ...'

Given our dependence on water for domestic use, you would think it would be important for us to keep our lakes and rivers as clean as possible. Sadly, clean water has not always been a prime consideration for society. Too often lakes and rivers have become the dumping ground for waste products, thereby polluting the very water we need to keep clean (Figure 6.4).

◉ From what you know from Table 2.1 about the three main categories of water usage, can you suggest what the three main sources of pollution are likely to be?

○ Industrial waste, domestic waste (sewage) and agricultural waste (such as the soluble waste from fertilizers).

You know already, from Section 4.4.1, that water used for human consumption needs to be of a certain quality, in other words — potable. In Section 6.3.1 we look in more detail at the ways in which potable water may be rendered unfit for human consumption (or, indeed, consumption by other animals) as the result of pollution.

6.3.1 The causes and effects of water pollution

Industrial pollution has often arisen in the past as the result of ignorance. Industries were frequently permitted to discharge their untreated waste products into lakes and rivers. Only later did the harmful consequences of these products become apparent. Figure 6.5 shows a warning notice advising people not to catch fish from a river in Florida, USA. For many years this river received untreated waste, which contained extremely toxic chemicals, from a wood-pulp mill. In other instances, the discharge of harmful substances into our waterways is less obvious; for example, rainwater seeping through the waste-tips of old lead mines dissolves the lead, and carries it into rivers.

Figure 6.5 Warning notice by the side of a river in Florida, USA.

Among the pollutants from industry are metals such as lead and mercury, which are toxic above a certain concentration. Once they get into the water cycle, they begin to accumulate at various points along the way. They become incorporated into the muds of lakes and estuaries, and they build up in the tissues of plants and animals that live in the water or grub in the mud for their food. As these organisms are eaten by others, the metals become steadily more concentrated in the tissues of the predators until they reach levels that may become life-threatening. If we eat fish and shellfish from these polluted waters, then the lead and mercury will find their way into our bodies, too.

It isn't only industry that is responsible for polluting our lakes and rivers with metals. Individual human beings are equally culpable. In 1979 it was estimated that around 3 000 mute swans in the UK could be dying of poisoning as the result of eating the lead weights that were carelessly discarded by anglers after a day's fishing. Fortunately this number has decreased significantly now that weights are made of different materials. You don't have to be an angler, however, to contaminate the water supply with lead. If you drive a car that uses leaded petrol, then some of this lead is likely to end up washed into rivers and lakes. You may also live in a house that still contains lead water pipes. As water passes through the pipes, a little of the lead is dissolved and so enters the water cycle. One side effect of both lead and mercury poisoning is brain damage. You may already know that the saying 'as mad as a hatter' is derived from the days when mercury was used in the manufacture of men's top hats.

Pollution from domestic sewage can lead to more than one sort of problem. Most obviously, sewage is a source of water-borne diseases such as cholera and typhoid fever (Section 4.4.1). A second problem with sewage is that it is broken down in water by bacteria that use the oxygen, dissolved in the water, for respiration. This same dissolved oxygen also supports the other aquatic life. The more sewage there is in the water, the more bacteria are required to break it down, and so the less oxygen there is for fish and other aquatic animals. Once the oxygen in the water is used up, it isn't long before the water begins to smell distinctly unpleasant due to the gases released when the sewage begins to be broken down by bacteria that can live without oxygen. If you've ever stirred up the mud at the bottom of a stagnant pond, you will know exactly what we mean.

Agricultural activities pose problems through both crop spraying and the use of fertilizers. Crop spraying is carried out to prevent damage to crops from weeds and various forms of pests (Figure 6.6). However, such spraying can disperse herbicides and pesticides over a wide area so that they end up in water that drains into rivers and lakes. In high enough doses these pollutants may be toxic and, like lead and mercury, they can accumulate in the tissues of animals and so end up in our bodies too.

Figure 6.6 Pesticide being sprayed onto fruit trees in the area of the Po delta, northern Italy. Over 7 000 kg of pesticide end up in the Po river every year. Underground water is also affected and hundreds of wells have become so contaminated that they have been sealed off.

In Section 4.4.1 we mentioned one of the problems caused by pollution from fertilizers. As well as nitrogen, fertilizers contain other nutrients, substances essential for the healthy growth of all plants and animals. One trouble is that a lot of fertilizer seeps into lakes and rivers by drainage off the land and it can lead to excessive plant growth. As a lake surface becomes covered with water weed, oxygen can no longer be dissolved in the water to replenish what is being used by fish and other aquatic animals. Once again, starved of oxygen, the animal life soon begins to die, and the water becomes stagnant and foul-smelling.

Our discussion of the effects of water pollution has a taken up a lot of space with words. The notion that a single diagram can summarize a piece of text was described in Section 4.5. In Figure 6.7 we have summarized how lead may get into lakes and rivers, and some of its effects. Figure 6.7 is a form of *flow diagram*. The arrows show the routes taken by lead from its various sources into the water cycle, and then into plant and animal life. Study it carefully.

Figure 6.7 A diagrammatic summary of some sources of lead in lakes and rivers, and some of the organisms that accumulate the lead.

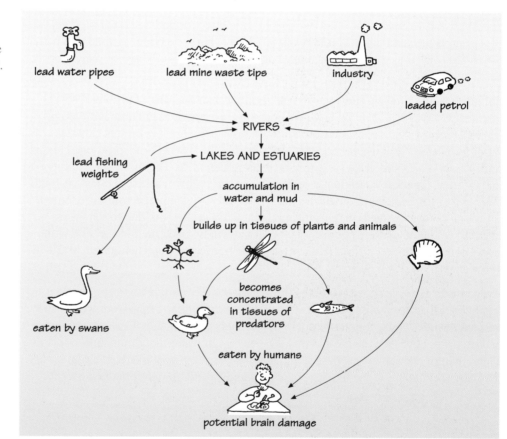

Activity 6.2 Summarizing text with a diagram

When you did Activity 4.8 you translated a diagram into text. In this activity we ask you to do the reverse. ◄

6.3.2 The pollution of the River Thames: a case study

Pollution from domestic sewage entering waterways was a very serious problem in large cities in Britain during the 19th century, and one which was not alleviated until the later part of the 20th century. Pollution of the River Thames in London is a case in point. We shall use this river as a case study that explores the life of a large river and that is typical of the conditions of large rivers throughout the world.

In 1596, when the poet Edmund Spenser penned the line 'Sweet Thames run softly, till I end my song' as the recurring refrain in 'Prothalamion', it is very likely that the Thames was a 'sweet' and clean-flowing river. Although it was common practice in Spenser's day for people to take their buckets of sewage down to the Thames to empty, and then refill with the river water for domestic use, the population of London was sufficiently small for the oxygen dissolved in the water to be replenished as fast as the bacteria breaking the sewage down were able to use the oxygen up. However, as the population of London expanded during the 19th century when people were driven off the land by the Enclosures Act, and as flush sanitation was installed in houses leading to the direct discharge of sewage into the river, a different story emerged. The insanitary conditions of Thames water seriously affected the health of people living in London, with five cholera epidemics occurring between 1830 and 1871.* The filthy state of the Thames was the focus of satire for cartoonists of this period (Figures 4.13 and 6.8).

Figure 6.8   Cartoon from *Punch* of 1855 showing the physicist, Michael Faraday, greeting an offensively smelling King Neptune in the Thames.

The oxygen levels in the water as the Thames passed through London became so depleted that in the drought summer of 1858 the river was rendered lifeless. The problem was exacerbated by the fact that the Thames is still tidal in central London. This means that some of the raw sewage transported down river from London was washed back up again on the incoming tide. The stench from the river became unbearable and on occasions Parliament had to be abandoned. This was no bad thing because, following this so-called 'Year of the Great Stink', Parliament was forced to take steps to find a remedy.

*The date *1830* appears in a discussion of the *19*th century, because our years are numbered according to a convention based in Christian tradition. The numbers represent the years that, traditionally, are considered to have elapsed since Christ was born. Consequently, all dates from 1 AD to 100 AD (AD = *Anno Domini*, 'in the year of our Lord') are said to occur within the *first* century AD, and those from 101 AD to 200 AD occur within the *second* century AD. So, the end of the century is marked by years such as 100, 200, 1900, 2000.

Figure 6.9 is a graph showing the dissolved oxygen content of the Thames at various distances upstream and downstream from London Bridge in 1893, 1970 and 1992. Like several of the other illustrations you have met in the book, this one requires some close reading.

Figure 6.9 A graph showing the average dissolved oxygen content (as a percentage of saturation) of the River Thames at various distances upstream and downstream from London Bridge in 1893, 1970 and 1992. Measurements were taken during July–October, when pollution is greatest.

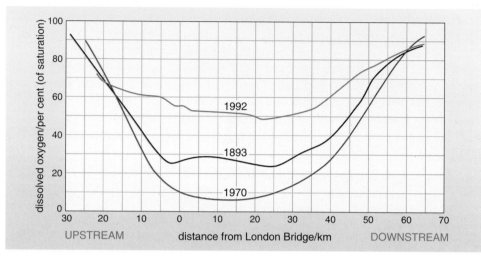

The vertical scale shows the dissolved oxygen content in the Thames, expressed as a percentage of the oxygen level at **saturation**. When the water is holding as much oxygen as it can, it is said to be saturated with respect to oxygen, and the saturation level is 100%. The scale on the horizontal axis may appear strange to you, because the 0 km mark does not coincide with the intersection of the horizontal and vertical axes, as you might expect. London Bridge has been chosen as the zero reference point because it is not far from the centre of London. However, we want to be able to record changes in the oxygen content as relatively fresh Thames water flows into London, and as polluted water flows out of London. Consequently the horizontal scale needs to extend some distance both upstream and downstream of London Bridge.

Each of the curves records measurements of dissolved oxygen in the Thames during July to October in a particular year. There are some similarities between all three curves. You can see that 20 km upstream of London Bridge the river is fairly rich in oxygen (70–90% saturation). This is true for each of the three curves. As the water flows through London the oxygen levels fall and it is about 20–25 km downstream from London Bridge before oxygen levels begin building up again. However, the curves for the three years do not coincide, showing that the oxygen levels in the Thames where it flows through London have varied considerably. There are historical reasons for these differences.

During 1858, when pollution from sewage was at its worst, the oxygen levels downstream of London Bridge would have reached zero, but by 1893 they had improved significantly as the result of government legislation.

Question 6.10   What was the dissolved oxygen level 20 km downstream of London Bridge in 1893? ◄

Unfortunately, the very rapid growth of London in the first half of the 20th century meant that sewage treatment was unable to keep pace with the growing population, so oxygen levels plummeted once more, reaching zero again at London Bridge during the 1950s. However, after the 1960s, tighter controls on sewage discharge and improved treatment facilities brought about a steady improvement, and this is reflected in the curve for 1970.

⬤ Does the curve for 1970 represent an improvement or a deterioration in oxygen levels since 1893?

◯ It represents a deterioration because the curve for 1970 lies below that for 1893.

⬤ What were the oxygen levels between London Bridge and about 20 km downstream in 1970?

◯ They were between about 5% and 10% of the level at saturation.

Oxygen levels continued to improve during the late 20th century, and there was much rejoicing in the angling community when the first salmon for 141 years was caught in the Thames 20 km downstream of London Bridge in 1974. By 1992 this same stretch of the Thames was recording dissolved oxygen levels of between 50% and 60% of saturation. The story of the River Thames has a happy ending, but awareness of the problems of pollution has not been as high in some countries, as Figure 6.4 shows.

Activity 6.1   Listing key points (continued)

Remember to look back at your notes and highlighting in Section 6.3, and produce a list of the main points. ◀

Activity 5.1   Planning your study (continued)

Before leaving Section 6.3, check your log of study time and compare it with your work plan. Now would be a good time to adjust your plans, if necessary. ◀

6.4   A world where water is scarce

People who live in countries where water is in short supply are very careful about its use. However, many plants and animals have evolved various ways of surviving in conditions where there would not be enough water to sustain human life. Now that you have learned more about the science of water, let's return to the desert organisms introduced in Section 3.3, and consider in more detail how they are adapted to conditions where water is scarce.

6.4.1   Camels and cacti revisited

In Section 4.3 you learned that cooling by sweating is important because it prevents the body from overheating, which can damage its functioning. Humans readily sweat in order to maintain their normal body temperature of around 37 °C. This is important because if the body temperature rises to as high as 39.5 °C and stays there, the body functions become impaired and death follows. Such an efficient sweating mechanism depends critically on the availability of drinking water to replace water lost by sweating. However, the camel's normal body temperature of 38 °C can rise to about 40 °C before it begins to sweat, and therefore the amount of water lost by sweating is reduced. In fact, its body temperature can rise even higher than this — as high as 41.5 °C — without impairing its body functions.

A particularly vulnerable surface for water loss by evaporation is the inside of the lungs. Large quantities of air are breathed into the lungs and out to the external world every minute of the day and night. The air passes from the nose through the nasal passages, which are tubes at the back of the nose that connect to a tube that leads to the lungs. In the camel the nasal passages are long, narrow and elaborately convoluted. This means that they have a large total surface area of more than 1.0×10^3 cm², which can be pictured as the area of a strip of ribbon 10 m long and 1 cm wide. The structure of the nasal passages helps to conserve water at night when the air temperature in desert regions is much lower than during the day. At night, when the air temperature is about 25 °C or less, the convoluted nasal passages are cooled each time the inhaled air passes through them. Once in the lungs, the cool night air is warmed to the camel's body temperature. However, as the warmed air is exhaled, it is cooled by the lower temperature of the nasal passages. In the camel, the air leaves the lungs at a body temperature of 38 °C but, after passing through the convoluted nasal passages, its temperature is reduced to 25 °C. In animals such as humans, which have wide nasal passages, cooling of the nasal passages by the inhaled air is incomplete, and so the exhaled air leaving the nose is warmer than the surrounding air.

How does the process of cooling the exhaled air affect water retention in the camel?

As you discovered in Sections 4.1 and 4.5, cooler air cannot contain as much water vapour as warmer air. Consequently, some of the water vapour present in the air as it leaves the lungs will condense within the nasal passages instead of being lost to the atmosphere.

Although this water retention can only work when the surrounding air temperature is much lower than body temperature, it makes an important contribution to overall water conservation in camels. In addition, the camel's nasal passages are lined with mucus that absorbs water from the exhaled air.

Like animals, plants generally have a vulnerable surface for water loss by evaporation. Pores, called stomata, are present on stems and are particularly common on the surface of leaves. Stomata can open and close, and are important for air exchange. When open, they expose the inner layer of the leaves, making them vulnerable to water loss. In cacti, water is conserved because they have very many fewer stomata on stems than other kinds of plants, and the leaves are reduced to spines, which have no stomata at all. Cacti, like camels, also take advantage of the cool temperatures at night for conserving water. The stomata on the stems open only at night; during the heat of the day they remain closed.

6.4.2 The world of *Dune*

To end Section 6 we turn our attention to a fictional view of how human beings might survive in a world without any surface water or precipitation. This is the planet of Arrakis in the novel *Dune* by Frank Herbert. The only surface water on Arrakis is locked up in small polar ice-caps, so almost the whole of the planet is a permanent desert.

> The effect of Arrakis on the mind of the newcomer usually is that of overpowering barren land. The stranger might think nothing could live or grow in the open here, that this was the true wasteland that had never been fertile and never would be.

However, Arrakis *is* inhabited — by a race of people called the Fremen who have found ways of adapting both their clothing and their life-styles to survive in the extremely hot and arid environment. Through the mouth of one of his characters, Frank Herbert describes in some detail how the stillsuit, the protective clothing used in the desert environment, conserves body water. To appreciate this description, you have to be able to understand the scientific principles behind it. Many people who have read *Dune,* or who will read the book one day, have not studied much science, but you are more fortunate. The science you have studied so far in *Water for life* is sufficient for you to make sense of how a stillsuit works.

The stillsuit is absolutely essential for survival outdoors on Arrakis, where a person can lose up to 5 litres of water a day simply by sitting still in the shade. The stillsuit is an all-in-one body suit designed to reclaim all the water lost each day by the human body. Frank Herbert's description of how it works is reproduced below. Some parts of the original text have been omitted, because they are not relevant to the explanation. Where we have left text out, we have indicated this by inserting three dots (…). There will be some parts of the description that you probably won't understand fully; at least, not using just what you've learned from studying this block. Don't worry about this for the moment, just highlight or underline any words or terms that you do not understand as you read it through for the first time.

> It's basically a micro-sandwich — a high-efficiency filter and heat-exchange system … The skin-contact layer is porous. Perspiration passes through it, having cooled the body … The next two layers include heat-exchange filaments and salt precipitators. Salt's reclaimed … Motions of the body, especially breathing … and some osmotic action provide the pumping force … Reclaimed water circulates to catch-pockets from which you draw it through this tube in the clip at your neck … Urine and faeces are processed in the thigh pads … In the open desert, you wear this filter across your face, this tube in the nostrils with these plugs to ensure a tight fit. Breathe in through the mouth filter, out through the nose tube. With a Fremen suit in good working order, you won't lose more than a thimbleful of moisture a day …

For the time being we shall concentrate on those parts of the stillsuit description that you should be able to understand.

Activity 6.3   Using existing knowledge to understand new material

This activity requires you to answer some questions on the above extract. In doing so, you will find that you are also revising material that you studied earlier in this block. ◀

Now that you have worked through Activity 6.3 you should have a good understanding of how the fictional stillsuit conserves body water, but what about the words or terms that you did not understand? Box 6.3, *Coping with scientific text that you don't understand*, should help you to handle these.

Box 6.3   Coping with scientific text that you don't understand

From time to time, we all come across scientific text that we don't understand. This is perfectly normal. You shouldn't expect to be able to understand *everything* you read, especially the first time you read it. If you did, you would probably have no learning left to do. We have tried to write the books for *Discovering Science* in a way that most students will understand, but everyone is different, and some parts of the course will prove harder to understand for some people than others. If you read relevant scientific articles outside of the course, for example the science pages of the broadsheet newspapers, or popular scientific journals like *New Scientist* that can be bought at larger newsagents, then you will almost certainly find some terms and concepts in them that mean little to you. This doesn't matter, provided you can make sense in a general way of what the article is trying to tell you.

Let's look back at the extract from *Dune* on the previous page.

○ Which terms did you highlight, or underline, because you didn't understand them? How much did your lack of understanding of these terms detract from your ability to understand the scientific principles behind the operation of a stillsuit?

○ The chances are that you highlighted some or all of 'micro-sandwich', 'heat-exchange system' and 'heat-exchange filaments', 'salt precipitators' and 'osmotic action'. If you were able to respond to parts (c)–(f) of Activity 6.3 satisfactorily, or to follow our comments if you didn't manage to work out the responses for yourself, then a lack of understanding of some of these terms didn't prevent you from understanding the scientific principles behind the stillsuit.

When you come across new terms in your reading that aren't explained, then the first thing you might do is to look the word, or words, up in a dictionary. Let's try this with the word 'precipitator'. To begin with, you would look up precipitate. A dictionary is likely to include several definitions of precipitate, such as: 'to hurl headlong', 'to condense and fall as rain, snow etc.' (remember that rain and snow are collectively called precipitation), and 'to come out of solution'. The first two of these definitions are obviously not appropriate. However, you know that salt will go into solution, i.e. dissolve, and so it would seem reasonable to assume that a salt precipitator is something that will bring salt out of solution. It would be worth noting this in the margin to remind you if you refer back to this passage.

Using the dictionary doesn't always help, though. If you try looking up 'osmotic', you will have to search for it under 'osmosis'. A dictionary definition of this word is: 'diffusion of liquids through a porous septum'. The

chances are, you might be none the wiser! You might then need to look up 'diffusion', 'porous' and 'septum'.

A second approach is to see whether you can make an 'educated guess' at what words mean. You could do this, for example, with 'micro-sandwich'. You probably know that 'micro' means something extremely small. A *micro*scope allows you to see objects that are too small to see with the naked eye. A *micro*be is a microscopic organism, and a *micro*chip is the tiny silicon chip at the heart of your computer. A sandwich, of course, is something that is layered. So a micro-sandwich is likely to be either a very small sandwich (unlikely in the context of the stillsuit description!), or something that has very small layers. As you read on through the extract, it's clear that the latter is a more reasonable guess. You learn that the stillsuit has three layers, the 'skin-contact' layer and two more. In this context the term 'micro' probably means that each of the layers is very *thin*, rather than very small.

What about the remaining two terms? You might suggest that the 'heat-exchange system' has something to do with the fact that as perspiration is evaporated, the body cools down. It won't affect your understanding of the way the stillsuit conserves and recycles the body's water if this is wrong. Similarly, it doesn't matter if, in the end, you don't know what 'osmotic action' means. The important point is that somehow water is being pumped from where it is being produced, to wherever it has to be processed, and then on to the catch-pockets for re-use.

When you are studying your course texts, it is obviously very important if you can't understand something that forms the basis of an argument which is being developed throughout a large section of the text. As you won't get far until you do understand it, you will need to contact your tutor-counsellor or another student in your study group. If your progress isn't going to be impeded, then it is not worth wasting time struggling to understand what you haven't grasped at the first couple of attempts. It is better to make a note in the margin and carry on with what comes next, and to sort out the problem at a later date.

You should be in a position now to pull together some of the threads of Sections 6.4.1 and 6.4.2, along with information presented earlier in this book (Section 3.3), and to present them in writing in a concise and coherent way for someone else to read. You have already looked at a fictional way in which human beings might minimize their water loss in the hot desert. In the next activity we are going to ask you to think about the problems of water loss for camels in a hot desert environment, and how these are overcome.

Activity 6.4 Making notes and using them to write an account

In this activity you will write a brief account of the camel's ability to survive the shortage of water in a hot desert environment. ◄

Activity 6.5 Writing concisely: how camels survive shortage of water

This activity requires you to look at an extract from an overlength account of how camels survive the shortage of water, and to suggest how it could be made more concise. ◄

Activity 6.6 Communicating science: how camels survive shortage of water

This activity requires you to read critically another student's account of how camels survive the shortage of water and to watch a video of students discussing how this account could be improved. Critical discussion of writing is a good way to develop writing skills. ◄

Activity 6.1 Listing key points (continued)

After completing Section 6.4, look back at your notes and highlighting in Section 6.4, and produce a list of the main points of this section. ◄

6.5 Summary of Section 6

Activity 6.7 Summarizing a section

You should now use the notes you have made of the main points of each of Sections 6.1–6.4 to produce a summary of the whole of Section 6. You should write the summary in concise sentences, rather than notes. When you have completed your summary, compare it with the version that we have prepared (in the comments on this activity). ◄

For completeness a summary of the skills that have been developed in Section 6 is given below.

Powers of ten are a convenient way of expressing very large or very small numbers, and indicate how many times a number has to be either multiplied by 10 or divided by 10 to obtain the final number.

In scientific notation the number attached to the power of ten is less than 10 but greater than or equal to 1.

Diagrams can be used in scientific writing to summarize text and make a passage of text easier to understand.

It is not necessary to understand every word in a passage of text you read, provided that you can make sense of what is written. Approaches to unfamiliar words include looking them up in a dictionary, and making educated guesses about their meanings.

Activity 5.1 Planning your study (continued)

Before leaving Section 6, check your log of study time and compare it with your work plan. Now would be a good time to adjust your plans, if necessary, for studying Section 7. ◄

7 Afterword

The *afterword* for this book, *Water for life,* is a brief section that asks you to think about what the 'science' in *Discovering Science* is all about, now that you have had a chance to study some. We shall mention briefly the main activities of science and scientists, and the responsibilities of scientists.

7.1 The activities of scientists

If you look up the word 'science' in the dictionary, it generally gives the most common meaning: the organized body of information about the material world that has been obtained by experiment and observation. There are other, older meanings. At one time it meant *all* knowledge. This, indeed, is where the word comes from: the Latin for 'knowledge' is *scientia.*

People acquire knowledge as scientists by engaging in four fundamentally important activities. You have been introduced to these activities while working through this book. The first is *observation*; scientists observe the natural world around them and describe what they see. Second, they try to construct *hypotheses* to explain or make sense of what they see; the archaeologists who discovered our friend Bones in the Egyptian desert (Figure 2.1) may have erected more than one hypothesis that could explain how she came to be buried there. Third, they carry out *experiments*, where possible, to test their hypotheses. The experiment you carried out in Activity 3.2 not only tested the hypothesis that potatoes, like cabbages and cucumbers, contain water, but also helped to establish roughly what percentage of a potato's mass is water. Once a hypothesis has been tested, by experiments where possible, and is found to be consistent with a wide range of observations, it becomes a **scientific theory**. Finally, scientists must be able to *communicate their findings* to other people, both to raise public awareness of new science, and so that other scientists can build on their work to extend knowledge still further. The importance of scientists being able to explain their science to other people mustn't be underestimated. For this reason you will find that throughout this course we place great emphasis on encouraging you to develop your communication skills.

Table 7.1 shows something of the parallel development of human communication and of science and its technological applications, set in the context of Earth history as a whole. The years before present (BP) shown in this table are, of course, approximate. In other words they imply 'about that long ago'. As far as the older times are concerned, clearly no scientist could prove that the Earth was formed *exactly* 4.6×10^9 years ago, or that the first human settlements were made 1.2×10^4 years ago. Similarly, the more recent times can't be given precisely because they depend on when you are studying *Discovering Science*. If you are studying in 1998, then the first fully-electronic computer would have been built 52 years ago. If you are studying in 2006, then 60 years ago would be more appropriate, so 50–60 years embraces almost all of our readers.

○ Looking at Table 7.1, how would you say the pace of scientific and technological development has changed over the past 1.2×10^4 years of human history?

○ After proceeding at a fairly slow and steady pace, it began to speed up about 500 years ago, and has continued to accelerate rapidly over the past 200 years.

Table 7.1 Some stages in the development of science and its technological applications, and human communication, set in the context of Earth and human history.

Years BP	Events in Earth history
4.6×10^9	Earth and planets in the Solar System formed
3.8×10^9	first evidence of life
4.4×10^8	evolution of first land plants
4.0×10^8	evolution of first land animals
3.0×10^6	evolution of first hominids (human-like animals)

Years BP	Developments in science and technology	Developments in communication
3.5×10^4		fluent human speech
1.2×10^4	first human settlements	
9.0×10^3	use of stone tools	
6.0×10^3		primitive writing based on pictures (Egypt and Mesopotamia)
5.8×10^3	first use of bronze (alloy of tin and copper)	
3.7×10^3		first alphabet developed (Palestine)
3.5×10^3	first use of iron	
2.6×10^3	era of Greek science, based on philosophy (Aristotle, Pythagoras)	
1.0×10^3		Chinese invented printing
7.0×10^2	experimental science of William of Occam	
5.0×10^2	Earth orbits the Sun (Copernicus)	first printing press (Caxton)
4.0×10^2	circulation of blood (Harvey)	
3.0×10^2	theory of gravity (Newton); invention of telescope	
2.0×10^2	Industrial Revolution (in Britain)	
1.5×10^2	theory of evolution by natural selection (Darwin); early railways	photography invented
1.0×10^2	first powered flight; theory of special relativity (Einstein)	wireless telegraphy invented
50–60		first fully-electronic computer
40–50	structure of DNA (Watson and Crick); first human in orbit (Gagarin)	
30–40	first human on the Moon (Armstrong)	computers with silicon chips
0–20	Human Genome Mapping Project; multiple organ transplants	lap-top computers; communications networking; the 'Internet'; artificial intelligence ('thinking' computers)

In Table 7.1 we have quoted the years that are 100 or more before present using powers of ten. This is not only to save space in the table; it is also so that we can see more clearly the increasing age of events as far back in time as the formation of the Solar System. It is easier to read the powers of ten than to count up a series of zeros to work out a large number. We explore the use of powers a little further in Box 7.1, *More about powers*.

Box 7.1   More about powers

You have seen in Boxes 6.1 and 6.2 that large and small numbers can conveniently be expressed in terms of powers of ten. For example,

123 000 000 can be written as 1.23×10^8

0.000 001 23 can be written as 1.23×10^{-6}

In this notation,

$$10^8 = 10 \times 10 \times 10 \times 10 \times 10 \times 10 \times 10 \times 10$$

so a positive power — 8 in this case — tells us how many tens we have to *multiply* together to get the required number. Similarly,

$$10^{-6} = 1 \div 10 \div 10 \div 10 \div 10 \div 10 \div 10$$

and so a negative power tells us how many times we need to *divide* by ten to get the required number. Also

$$10^{-6} = \frac{1}{10 \times 10 \times 10 \times 10 \times 10 \times 10} = \frac{1}{10^6}$$

The use of powers is not limited to the number 10 though; they can be used with any other number, and in this book you have already met a couple of examples of the use of powers in a completely different context. When we were discussing areas in Box 4.2, we said that the appropriate SI unit was square metres, and we abbreviated this to m².

● If $10^2 = 10 \times 10$, what is m² is equal to?

○ m² = m × m.

The power '2' has the same meaning in each case: it means multiply together 2 of the numbers or unit abbreviations, or whatever the power is attached to. When calculating an area, the sort of sum we do is 3 m × 4 m = (3 × 4) × (m × m) = 12 m². The reason for abbreviating square metres to m² is clear from this; it is just another way of writing m × m, and it has the advantage of conciseness.

We also used a power of 'm' when discussing the unit of volume in the metric system of units (Box 4.2). In that case we were talking about cubic metres, m × m × m, and this was abbreviated to m³. This is consistent with what we have said about the meaning of a positive power — it's how many of the letter m that we have to multiply together.

Question 7.1   Work out the values of the following numbers: (a) 2^3; (b) 3^2; (c) 2^5; (d) 4^2. ◀

Question 7.2   Write the following using the power notation. (For example, $7 \times 7 \times 7 = 7^3$.)
(a) $8 \times 8 \times 8 \times 8$; (b) 5×5; (c) $3 \times 3 \times 3 \times 3 \times 3$; (d) m × m × m × m. ◀

What about negative powers? Well, they too can be applied to any number or unit abbreviation. The meaning of negative powers is analogous to their meaning when they are applied to the number 10. For powers of ten,

10^{-3} is the same as $\frac{1}{10^3}$.

● What is the value of 2^{-3}?

○ $2^{-3} = 1 \div 2 \div 2 \div 2 = \frac{1}{2 \times 2 \times 2} = \frac{1}{2^3} = \frac{1}{8}$

So when the power is −3, the negative sign means 'divide by', and the number 3 tells you that you have to divide three times. This answer also makes it clear that

$$2^{-3} = \frac{1}{2^3}$$

Negative powers can also be used with symbols and units. Thus:

$$m^{-3} = 1 \div m \div m \div m = \frac{1}{m \times m \times m} = \frac{1}{m^3}$$

This way of converting between positive and negative powers is often used when expressing units concisely. Let's take an example that you have already met, the unit of density, which is kilograms per cubic metre in SI units, or kg per m³. Now kg 'per m³' means kg 'divided by m³', so this unit is kg/m³ or $\frac{kg}{m^3}$.

⬤ Can you see a way to rewrite $\dfrac{\text{kg}}{\text{m}^3}$ using a negative power?

⬤ Since $\dfrac{1}{\text{m}^3} = \text{m}^{-3}$, it can be written as kg m^{-3}.

The conventional scientific way of expressing the units of density is kg m^{-3}, and during the course you will meet a variety of examples of units of measurement that are expressed in a similar way using positive and negative powers.

Notice that we have left a space between kg and m^{-3} in the unit of density, and we do this whenever we write a unit that is a combination of two (or more) other units. This is different from the way that prefixes for multiples and sub-multiples of units are written; they are always written *without* a space between the prefix and the basic unit. For example, 'cm' means 'centimetre', which is a sub-multiple of a metre. Therefore, the unit of density is kg m^{-3}, and *not* kgm^{-3}, nor k gm^{-3}. This separation of the different components of the unit of density, but not of multiples of units, avoids confusion. To give another example, 'ms' means 'millisecond', but 'm s' means 'metre second'.

Question 7.3 Write each of the following as a fraction and as a decimal number: (a) 2^{-1}; (b) 4^{-2}; (c) 5^{-3}. ◀

Question 7.4 Write each of the following using both positive and negative power notation.
For example,

$$\frac{1}{5} \times \frac{1}{5} = \frac{1}{5^2} = 5^{-2}$$

(a) $\dfrac{1}{2 \times 2 \times 2 \times 2}$

(b) $1 \div 3 \div 3 \div 3 \div 3 \div 3$

(c) $\dfrac{1}{\text{m} \times \text{m}}$ ◀

Question 7.5 Express the following units using negative powers:

(a) kilograms per square metre (this unit is often used when selling sheets of wood, metal, paper, etc.);

(b) metres per second (unit of speed, like miles per hour);

(c) milligrams per litre (unit used for the quantity of calcium in bottled water in Figure 4.14). ◀

To return to the pace of scientific and technological development, it is interesting to note that when Frank Herbert wrote *Dune* (probably during 1964, as the book was first published in 1965), the first human had gone into orbit round the Earth, but no one had yet landed on the Moon. The idea of anyone needing anything like a stillsuit was fairly unlikely. Such is the pace of technological development that the notion of maintaining viable space stations on the surface of a planet such as Mars is now a serious scientific possibility, and not just a twinkle in the eye of a science fiction writer. But for humans to survive for long periods in space, they will require systems that will reclaim and recycle water very efficiently, though perhaps not as efficiently as a Fremen stillsuit!

In the late 20th century a good deal of research was being carried out into what are called closed ecological systems. These are small communities of plants and animals (including humans) that are closed off from the outside world, and in which oxygen, water and nutrients are recycled. One system being modelled by computer in 1992 involved reclaiming water from both plant and animal waste. In this model, the inedible matter from plants in the system's crop growing unit was processed to remove the water. The residue, together with paper and plastic waste and faeces, was incinerated. Water lost through breathing, sweating and urinating, together with domestic waste water from showers, etc., was collected in an evaporator. Here it came into contact with hot gases produced during the incineration of the solid waste. The heat evaporated the water, thereby purifying it because the insoluble and unwanted residues were left behind. The purified water could then be reused for human consumption.

7.2 The responsibilities of scientists

The activities of scientists have led, and will continue to lead, to ever increasing knowledge of our world. This knowledge has the potential to create untold benefits for humankind, but also has the potential for inflicting unimaginable harm. It is therefore an important responsibility of scientists to try to maximize the former and to minimize the latter.

The idea that scientists have responsibilities to society is something we should like you to keep in mind as you work through this course. For the most part, scientists want their discoveries to be used to benefit humankind. Occasionally choices are made that result in knowledge being used in ways that might be considered detrimental.

○ Can you think of one or two examples of ways in which science has been used specifically for the benefit of humankind, and one or two ways in which its use has been detrimental?

○ You might have come up with the science associated with medical research or some aspects of agriculture as beneficial, and developments in atomic, biological or chemical warfare as detrimental.

There are many instances where scientific knowledge has been used in what scientists *believed* were our best interests, but that later turned out to have some damaging consequences for the environment. One such example is our use of fuels, such as coal and oil, to generate electricity. Most of us would regard electricity as beneficial to society. However, the burning of these fuels releases the gas carbon dioxide into the atmosphere and this gas may be influencing world climates adversely — a topic that we consider in Block 2.

Question 7.6   From what you have read in Section 6.3, can you recall some other examples of areas where scientific developments have had unintentionally damaging consequences? ◄

Unintentional damage is an ongoing hazard of scientific and technological development. In the mid- to late 1990s, scientific research began to uncover an increase in sterility and sexual abnormality in male fish living in rivers and lakes polluted by certain types of industrial chemicals. Parallel studies of human males across Europe, including Britain, also suggested an increase in potential sterility, and an increase in those born with sexual abnormalities, since the 1970s. The chemicals suspected of causing these harmful effects have a structure which is very similar to that of oestrogen (pronounced 'east-roe-jen'), the predominantly female hormone used in many women's contraceptive pills. As these chemicals are very widespread — from the manufacture of plastics, carpets and wood-pulp to ingredients in paints, industrial detergents and pesticides — eliminating them from the environment is not easy.

Fortunately, the great rise of environmental awareness during the 1980s and 1990s has encouraged many scientists to use their knowledge to find ways of putting past damage to rights, and of managing the environment more effectively. But it isn't only scientists who have a part to play in this. From our discussions of water usage in Sections 2.3 and 6.2, and of water pollution in Section 6.3, you will be aware that *everyone* has a responsibility to use knowledge to manage the environment and its resources more effectively.

Part of the responsibility of being a scientist is trying to predict the long-term effects of the possible uses of scientific discoveries. This raises the question of whether knowledge should ever be suppressed if its knock-on effects might prove harmful to society. This is a question you might like to think about for yourself as you work your way through *Discovering Science*.

7.3 Summary of Section 7

Science is the organized body of information about the material world that has been obtained by observation and experimentation. The four main activities of scientists are observing, erecting hypotheses, testing by experiment and communicating knowledge.

There has been an acceleration in the pace of scientific and technological development over the past 12 000 years.

The possibilities of humans spending long periods in space have encouraged research into the development of closed ecological systems.

Scientific discoveries may be used for the benefit or harm of humankind, although harmful outcomes are sometimes unintentional. Effective management of the environment and its resources is the responsibility of everyone.

Powers can be used with numbers other than ten, and with any symbol or unit abbreviations.

Activity 7.1   *Reviewing your study of Block 1*

As you studied this block you were introduced to a number of techniques to help you to study and learn more effectively. The end of the block is a good time to reflect on which techniques have worked well for you, to review how well you have met the block objectives, and to do a bit more work on any areas that you are unsure about. This should be useful preparation for your study of Block 2. ◄

What to do now?

You have now completed Block 1 of *Discovering Science*. There are a number of other tasks that we recommend you carry out *before* you start Block 2, including setting up your computer and using it both to practise the maths skills introduced in Block 1, and to learn some new maths skills. You will find details of these tasks at the end of the activity notes in the Study File.

Questions: answers and comments

For mathematical answers we show all the steps in our working and we encourage you to do this too. This is good practice as it enables you to see where you went wrong if your answer is incorrect. When you submit answers to assignments that require some mathematics, it will be important to lay out your answers carefully, showing all the steps in your working. If your final numerical answer is wrong, you would still gain marks for showing that you understood what was required, and showing the steps also allows you and your tutor-counsellor to see where you went wrong in the calculation.

Many of the answers below contain extra 'comments', denoted {...}. These are points that we would not expect you to include in your answer; usually they reinforce the teaching.

Question 2.1 Among the questions that might have occurred to you are the following:

How long ago did Bones live?

What kind of civilization was Bones a part of?

Was this place desert when Bones died, or has the climate changed so that the region has become desert since that time?

If this region was desert when Bones died, was it irrigated so that it could support human habitation?

What sort of food did Bones eat?

You may well have thought of other equally valid questions. {Note how, in order to make the answer to this question clear, we have set it out as a *list* of questions, each of which starts on a new line.}

Question 2.2 (a) The number given in the second column of Table 2.1 on the same line as 'flushing lavatory' is 44, so the average person uses 44 litres of water per day for this purpose. {This corresponds to about 5 flushes of an average cistern.}

(b) The entry in the third row from the bottom of the first column of the table is 'agriculture', so the number 7, together with the table title and the column heading, tells us that the use of water for agriculture in the UK is equivalent to 7 litres per day for each person in the country.

Question 2.3 (a) 124; (b) 112; (c) 230 litres; {Here the two quantities that you added have the unit litres, so you need to include the litres in the answer.} (d) 1 012; (e) 21; (f) 374 metres; (g) 106 grams; (h) 69; {You do not have to press = after the first part (38 + 92), though if you do the final answer is the same; check this for yourself.}

Question 2.4 (a) 1 008; (b) 2 280; (c) 9 893; (d) 62 116 litres; {Remember to include the unit in the answer to balance the unit in the question.} (e) 2; (f) 8; (g) 7 metres; (h) 96; (i) 931.

Question 2.5 (a) $26 - 12 + 4 = 14 + 4 = 18$

(b) $16 + 12 \times 2 = 16 + (12 \times 2) = 16 + 24 = 40$ {We have added brackets in (b) because, although not necessary, they make the calculation look clearer.}

(c) $(16 + 12) \times 2 = 28 \times 2 = 56$

(d) $35 - 7 \times 2 = 35 - (7 \times 2) = 35 - 14 = 21$

(e) $(35 - 7) \times 2 = 28 \times 2 = 56$

(f) $180 \div 10 \times 3 = 18 \times 3 = 54$

(g) $180 \div (10 \times 3) = 180 \div 30 = 6$

(h) $(10 + 5) \times (3 + 1) = 15 \times 4 = 60$

Question 2.6 (a) The total domestic use of water per person per day in the UK is found by adding the first six numbers in Table 2.1, that is 44 litres + 23 litres + 16 litres + 1 litre + 4 litres + 48 litres, and this equals 136 litres. The non-domestic use is the sum of all of the other numbers in the table, which is 189 litres + 7 litres + 220 litres + 52 litres, and this is equal to 468 litres per day for each person in the UK. The overall total is thus 136 + 468 = 604 litres per person per day in the UK.

(b) The difference between non-domestic and domestic uses of water, both of which were calculated in part (a), is 468 litres − 136 litres, or 332 litres per person per day.

(c) The weekly usage will be seven times greater than the daily usage, so a week of baths and showers will require 23 litres × 7 = 161 litres. The annual usage will be 365 times greater than the daily usage, so this will be 23 litres × 365 = 8 395 litres. {If your answer is 8 372 litres, i.e. 161 litres × 52 weeks, then this is not accurate since 365 days = 52 weeks + 1 day. You need to add another 23 litres to your answer.}

(d) 220 litres of water are used per person per day in electricity generation, and 44 litres per person per day for domestic lavatories. So if the water for electricity generation were used to flush lavatories instead, it would be enough to provide for 220/44 days, which is 5 days' supply.

Question 2.7   (a) The annual use must be 365 times the daily use, and the use per person is found by dividing the family use by 4. So the calculation is $440 \times 365 \div 4 = 40\,150$. The annual use per person is therefore 40 150 litres.

(b) The three people use 150 litres of water each, or 150×3 litres in total. From this the amounts that they use for baths and showers must be subtracted, and the calculation is therefore: $150 \times 3 - 15 - 25 - 40 = 370$. So 370 litres are used for all other purposes. {You could have inserted brackets for clarity: $(150 \times 3) - 15 - 25 - 40 = 370$, but in this case they are not essential because the order of the operations follows the mathematical rules.}

(c) Table 2.1 shows that each day a 'typical' person uses 44 litres of water for lavatory flushing, 23 litres for baths and showers, and 16 litres in washing machines. Written mathematically this is $44 + 23 + 16$. Since a family of four 'typical' people would use four times this amount, the complete equation is $(44 + 23 + 16) \times 4 = 332$, so the family of four will typically use 332 litres per day for these purposes. {The brackets mean that the *total* use of water for these three purposes per person is multiplied by 4, and they are essential for indicating that the addition must be carried out before the multiplication.}

Question 2.8   (a) 70%; {Remember, to convert a fraction to a percentage you multiply it by 100%; so $\frac{7}{10}$ is equivalent to $\frac{7}{10} \times 100\% = \frac{700\%}{10} = 70\%$.}

(b) 45%; (c) 52%; (d) 63%; (e) 70%; (f) 150%. {Note that this last answer is greater than 100%, because the fraction 30/20 (or 3/2) is greater than 1.}

Question 2.9   (a) $60\% = \dfrac{60}{100} = \dfrac{6}{10} = \dfrac{3}{5}$

{Here we have first divided the top and the bottom of the sixty-hundredths (i.e. 60%) by 10, and then by 2. Remember that dividing (or multiplying) both the top and the bottom of a fraction by any number will produce an equivalent fraction. It is conventional to express fractions with the smallest possible numbers on the top and the bottom.}

(b) $64\% = \dfrac{64}{100} = \dfrac{32}{50} = \dfrac{16}{25}$

{Here we have divided the top and the bottom of 64/100 by 2 and then 2 again, which is the same as dividing by 4.}

(c) $65\% = \dfrac{65}{100} = \dfrac{13}{20}$

(d) $67\% = \dfrac{67}{100}$

{This time there are no whole numbers by which we can divide both 67 and 100 to produce smaller whole numbers on the top and the bottom.}

Question 2.10   (a) $\dfrac{2}{5} \times 20 = \dfrac{2 \times 20}{5} = \dfrac{2 \times 4}{1} = 8$

(b) $\dfrac{7}{8} \times 24 = \dfrac{7 \times 24}{8} = \dfrac{7 \times 3}{1} = 21$

(c) 15% of £60 is

$$\dfrac{15}{100} \times £60 = \dfrac{15 \times £60}{100} = \dfrac{15 \times £3}{5} = \dfrac{3 \times £3}{1} = £9$$

(d) $\dfrac{60}{100} \times 5\,\text{metres} = \dfrac{60 \times 5\,\text{metres}}{100}$

$= \dfrac{6 \times 5\,\text{metres}}{10} = \dfrac{6 \times 1\,\text{metres}}{2} = 3\,\text{metres}$

Question 2.11   (a) From Table 2.2, the saving from not using any water outside is 20 litres per day. Before the savings, the total daily use is 400 litres (found by adding all of the values in Table 2.2). Therefore the saving is:

as a fraction: $\dfrac{20\,\text{litres}}{400\,\text{litres}} = \dfrac{2}{40} = \dfrac{1}{20}$

{note that the unit cancels out}

as a ratio: $1 : 20$

as a percentage: $\dfrac{1}{20} \times 100\% = 5\%$

{this could have been calculated directly:

$\dfrac{20}{400} \times 100\% = 5\%$}

(b) The reduced daily amount of water used for baths and showers will be:

$\dfrac{2}{3} \times 96\,\text{litres} = \dfrac{2 \times 96}{3}\,\text{litres} = 2 \times 32\,\text{litres}$

$\{$or $\dfrac{192}{3}$ litres $\}$ = 64 litres

The saving is therefore 96 litres − 64 litres = 32 litres.

An alternative way to get this answer is to recognize that if the water use is reduced to $\frac{2}{3}$ of its normal value, then the saving must be $\frac{1}{3}$ of the normal value. So the daily saving is:

$$\frac{1}{3} \times 96 \text{ litres} = \frac{96}{3} \text{ litres} = 32 \text{ litres}.$$

This saving is:

as a fraction: $\dfrac{32 \text{ litres}}{400 \text{ litres}} = \dfrac{8}{100} = \dfrac{2}{25}$

$\{$the unit cancels out$\}$

as a ratio: $2 : 25$

as a percentage: $\dfrac{2}{25} \times 100\% = \dfrac{200\%}{25} = 8\%$

(c) By putting a 1-litre bottle in their cistern, the amount of water used per flush is reduced from the normal 10 litres to 9 litres, a saving of 1 litre. This saving is:

as a fraction: $\dfrac{1 \text{ litre}}{10 \text{ litres}} = \dfrac{1}{10}$

$\{$the unit cancels out$\}$

as a percentage: $\dfrac{1}{10} \times 100\% = \dfrac{100\%}{10} = 10\%$

(d) The daily saving will be $\frac{1}{10}$ of the daily use for flushing the lavatory, so this is

$$\frac{1}{10} \times 120 \text{ litres} = 12 \text{ litres}$$

This saving can again be expressed as a fraction, ratio, or percentage of the total daily use:

as a fraction: $\dfrac{12 \text{ litres}}{400 \text{ litres}} = \dfrac{3}{100}$

$\{$the unit cancels out$\}$

as a ratio: $3 : 100$

as a percentage: $\dfrac{3}{100} \times 100\% = 3\%$

Question 2.12   Table 2.4 shows that the savings are much easier to compare when expressed as percentages. The saving on water for lavatory flushing is lowest — 3% of the total use — followed by outside use (5%), and

the largest saving, of 8%, is in the use for baths and showers. The savings are not so easy to compare when expressed as fractions or ratios. Can you tell, for example, from a quick glance which of $\frac{1}{20}$, $\frac{2}{25}$ and $\frac{3}{100}$ is the largest and which the smallest?

Table 2.4   Water savings of the Browns.

Use of water	Fraction	Ratio	Percentage
outside use	$\frac{1}{20}$	$1 : 20$	5
bath/shower	$\frac{2}{25}$	$2 : 25$	8
flushing lavatory	$\frac{3}{100}$	$3 : 100$	3

Question 2.13   The Browns save 20 litres on outside use, 32 litres on baths and showers and 12 litres on lavatory flushing each day, which is a total saving of 64 litres. As a percentage of their normal daily use of 400 litres per day, this is:

$$\frac{64 \text{ litres}}{400 \text{ litres}} \times 100\% = \frac{64\%}{4} = 16\%$$

$\{$the unit cancels out$\}$

Their neighbours' savings are:

$$\frac{70 \text{ litres}}{500 \text{ litres}} \times 100\% = \frac{70\%}{5} = 14\%$$

$\{$the unit cancels out$\}$

So the Browns make the more significant saving as a percentage, even though they save 6 litres less each day than the Patels. $\{$Note that it is again easier to compare the savings expressed as percentages than if they were quoted as fractions: $\frac{64}{400}$ (or $\frac{4}{25}$) and $\frac{70}{500}$ (or $\frac{7}{50}$). Note also that we could have used a simpler way to calculate the Browns' percentage saving: we could add the percentage savings for the three different areas: 5% + 8% + 3% = 16%$\}$

Question 3.1   (a) 5 km = 5 000 m = 500 000 cm = 5 000 000 mm; $\{$There are 1 000 metres in 1 kilometre, so 5 km = 5 × 1 000 m = 5 000 m. There are 100 centimetres in a metre, so 5 000 m = 5 000 × 100 cm = 500 000 cm. Alternatively we could say that 100 000 cm = 1 km, so 5 km = 5 × 100 000 cm. And since 1 cm = 10 mm, 500 000 cm = 5 000 000 mm.$\}$

(b) 3 kg = 3 000 g = 3 000 000 mg; $\{$There are 1 000 g in 1 kilogram, and 1 000 000 milligrams in 1 kilogram.$\}$

(c) 25 s = 25 000 ms.

Question 3.2   (a) $4\,000\,\text{g} = 4\,\text{kg}$, since $1\,000\,\text{g} = 1\,\text{kg}$.
So the calculation becomes $7\,\text{kg} + 4\,\text{kg} = 11\,\text{kg}$.
Alternatively, we could calculate the answer in grams.
In this case, $7\,\text{kg} = 7\,000\,\text{g}$, and $7\,000\,\text{g} + 4\,000\,\text{g}$
$= 11\,000\,\text{g}$. {The two answers are clearly equivalent:
$11\,\text{kg} = 11\,000\,\text{g}$. Either one is correct.}

(b) $55\,\text{cm} - 40\,\text{mm} = 55\,\text{cm} - 4\,\text{cm} = 51\,\text{cm}$.
Alternatively, $550\,\text{mm} - 40\,\text{mm} = 510\,\text{mm}$.

(c) $20\,\text{s} - 1\,000\,\text{ms} = 20\,\text{s} - 1\,\text{s} = 19\,\text{s}$. Alternatively
$20\,000\,\text{ms} - 1\,000\,\text{ms} = 19\,000\,\text{ms}$.

Question 3.3   (a) 0.125; (b) 0.25; (c) 0.75; (d) 0.1;
(e) 0.2; (f) 0.3; (g) 0.01; (h) 0.03; (i) 0.05; (j) 0.003.
{In each case you can convert the fraction to the
equivalent decimal number by dividing the number on
the top of the fraction by the number on the bottom. For
example, to calculate the decimal number equivalent to
$\frac{1}{8}$ using your calculator, you would press the keys in the
sequence $\boxed{1}\ \boxed{\div}\ \boxed{8}\ \boxed{=}$. The answers to parts (d)–(f)
highlight the fact that the first number after the decimal
point tells us the 'number of tenths'. Similarly parts
(g)–(i) show that the second number after the decimal
point indicates the 'number of hundredths'.}

Question 3.4   (a) $0.7 = \dfrac{7}{10}$

(b) $0.8 = \dfrac{8}{10} = \dfrac{4}{5}$

(c) $0.2 = \dfrac{2}{10} = \dfrac{1}{5}$

(d) $0.22 = \dfrac{22}{100} = \dfrac{11}{50}$

(e) $0.222 = \dfrac{222}{1000} = \dfrac{111}{500}$

{Remember, to convert a decimal number between 0 and
1 to a fraction you write the digits that follow the
decimal point on the top of the fraction, and on the
bottom of the fraction you write a 1 followed by the
same number of zeros as there are digits following the
decimal point. So for 0.222, you write 222 on the top of
the fraction, and $1\,000$ on the bottom — three zeros on
the bottom because there are three digits on the top of
the fraction.}

Question 3.5   (a) 14.11; (b) 10.37; (c) 6.71; (d) 18.1.
{For each of these calculations, you need to key in the
digits, decimal point, and +, −, ×, or ÷ symbol in the

order written in the question, followed by an = sign, and
the answer will appear in the display.}

Question 3.6   (a) 0.3; 0.26; 0.265. (b) 0.8; 0.83; 0.826.
(c) 21.1; 21.12; 21.118. {In each case, if the first digit
removed is a 5, 6, 7, 8 or 9, then the last digit remaining
is rounded up to the next highest digit. Thus when
0.264 8 is rounded to one decimal place, the 2 is rounded
up to 3 because the first of the three digits removed is 6.
However if the first digit removed is 0, 1, 2, 3 or 4, then
the last digit remaining is left unchanged.}

Question 3.7   (a) The subject of the graph is the
volume of water flowing each second past a point in a
stream after a rain storm. {The title or caption is usually
the best place to find out what a graph is showing.}

(b) Water flow, measured in litres per second, is plotted
on the vertical axis.

(c) Time is plotted on the horizontal axis, and this is
measured in hours. {The 24-hour clock has been used,
so the period covered is 1 day.}

(d) At 12.00 hours the water flow was about 95 litres per
second. {To find this flow, you first locate 12.00 hours
on the horizontal axis, then draw a line (real or
imaginary) from there up to the point where it intersects
the curve. From this point you then draw a horizontal
line to meet the vertical axis, and you read the
appropriate flow from the scale. In this case the line
intersects the scale one division below 100. Since
10 divisions correspond to 50 litres per second,
1 division corresponds to 5 litres per second, and so the
flow is $(100 - 5)$ litres per second, or 95 litres per
second.}

(e) The maximum flow is about 155 litres per second,
and this occurs at approximately 08.00 hours. {The
maximum flow corresponds to the peak of the curve; by
drawing horizontal and vertical lines from the peak to
the axes you can read off the flow and the time,
respectively.}

(f) The flow was steady until 04.00 hours, and it then
increased very rapidly for about an hour. After this it
increased more slowly until it reached a maximum flow
at 08.00 hours. It then started to decrease; there was a
small peak at about 11.00 hours, and the flow gradually
decreased until it became fairly steady after 20.00 hours.

Question 3.8 (a) After 6 minutes the mass of the cucumber was about 145 grams. {The way that you find this value is shown in Figure 3.6. You first locate 6 minutes along the (horizontal) time axis, indicated by the arrow labelled A; from here you move vertically up the graph until you reach the plotted data point, arrow B; you then move from arrow B horizontally across the graph to the vertical axis to read off the mass, arrow C. This is $2\frac{1}{2}$ divisions (millimetres) above 140. Since each centimetre on the vertical scale corresponds to 20 g, each millimetre division must correspond to 2 g. So 2.5 mm on the vertical scale corresponds to 2.5×2 g, i.e. 5 g. Therefore arrow C is at $(140 + 5)$ g.}

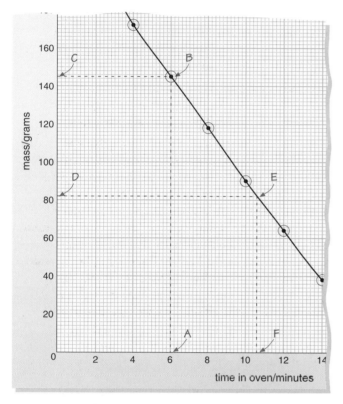

Figure 3.6 How to read values from Figure 3.4 to get the answers to Question 3.8.

(b) It took 10.6 minutes for the mass to fall to 82 grams. {Here you have to start by locating 82 grams on the (vertical) mass axis. This will be one division above the 80 g line. This is indicated by the arrow labelled D in Figure 3.6. From arrow D you move horizontally across the graph to reach the plotted line, arrow E, and from there you move vertically down to the time axis, arrow F. This is three divisions to the right of the 10 minute mark on the scale. Each centimetre on the time axis corresponds to 2 minutes, so each millimetre division

must be 0.2 minutes. Three divisions is therefore 0.6 minutes, so the time corresponding to arrow F is 10 minutes + 0.6 minutes = 10.6 minutes.}

Question 3.9 (a) The initial mass is the mass at zero minutes, which is the value on the vertical axis. This mass is 216 grams. The mass of the dried cucumber corresponds to the value at times greater than 20 minutes; all of the water has been removed by this stage, so the mass is approximately constant (the graph levels off) and has a value of about 7 grams. The difference between these two masses, 216 grams − 7 grams = 209 grams, is the mass of water in the cucumber.

(b) The percentage of cucumber that was water is calculated in exactly the same way as for the potato:

$$\text{percentage water} = \frac{\text{mass of water in cucumber}}{\text{initial mass of cucumber}} \times 100\%$$

From part (a), the mass of water in the cucumber was 209 grams, and the initial mass of cucumber was 216 grams, so

$$\text{percentage water} = \frac{209\,\text{grams}}{216\,\text{grams}} \times 100\% = 96.759\,259\%$$

{Note how the grams cancel out here. The accuracy with which the masses can be read from the graph does not justify quoting the answer to 6 decimal places, and so it is more appropriate to round the answer to the nearest whole number, that is 97%. We shall discuss how to decide on the appropriate number of decimal places to use later in the course.}

Question 4.1 A solid, like a piece of iron, is rigid — it has a shape and a volume that stay the same when you pick it up and handle it, and it keeps its shape irrespective of where it is placed. A liquid, like cooking oil, has a fixed volume, but has no shape of its own; its shape depends on the shape of the container into which it is put. {You can't pick up oil without using some sort of container. When you pour it from a bottle into a pan, the oil flows and changes its shape but the volume of the oil doesn't change; it has the same volume in the pan as it had in the bottle.} A gas, like air, has no fixed shape, and nor does it have a fixed volume. It also flows, like a liquid, and takes the shape of its container — for example, think of blowing up a balloon. What distinguishes a gas from a liquid is that a gas fills the whole volume of its container *completely*: it doesn't just remain in a fixed volume at the bottom of the container.

Question 4.2   (a) 65 °C; (b) 57 °C; (c) −57 °C; (d) 65 °C. {Positive temperatures are higher than negative temperatures. When two negative temperatures are compared, the one with the smaller number following the minus sign is hotter, e.g. −10 °C is hotter than −20 °C.}

Question 4.3   −210 °C, −85 °C, −27 °C, −26 °C, 0 °C, 85 °C, 210 °C, 1 750 °C. {Note that the negative temperatures are lower than the positive temperatures, and the larger the number following the minus sign the lower is the temperature, e.g. −20 °C is lower than −10 °C. Above 0 °C, higher numbers mean hotter temperatures, e.g. 20 °C is hotter than 10 °C.}

Question 4.4   Area of the bottom of the pool is 6 m × 7 m = 42 m^2.

Volume of the swimming pool is 6 m × 7 m × 2 m = 84 m^3.

Question 4.5   Since 1 000 litres = 1 m^3, then 2.5 million litres or 2 500 000 litres = 2 500 × 1 000 litres = 2 500 × 1 m^3 = 2 500 m^3.

Question 4.6   The volume of the aluminium block is 0.50 m × 0.30 m × 0.20 m = 0.030 m^3, so its density is 81 kg/0.030 m^3 = 2 700 kg/m^3. The volume of the lead block is 0.50 m × 0.50 m × 0.20 m = 0.050 m^3, so the density of lead is 570 kg/0.050 m^3 = 11 400 kg/m^3. Both blocks will sink because their density is greater than that of water.

{You may have noticed that your calculator didn't display the final zeros in the values of the two volumes, 0.030 m^3 and 0.050 m^3; you will see why these zeros are significant and have been included in our answer when you study Block 2, Box 2.1, *Uncertainty and significant figures.*}

Question 4.7   Evaporation of water can occur at temperatures other than the boiling temperature. Several examples in the text illustrate this: evaporation of sweat from the body; evaporation of perfume or aftershave on the skin; cooling a bottle of wine or fruit juice by wrapping it in a wet towel and placing it on a window ledge; and drying of a puddle. In all these examples evaporation occurs at various temperatures that are below the normal boiling temperature of 100 °C.

Question 4.8   Water (a) contains 117 mg/litre of calcium, while water (b) contains 30 mg/litre. So water

(a) contains $\dfrac{117 \text{ mg per litre}}{30 \text{ mg per litre}}$

= 3.9 times as much calcium as water (b). {Note that the unit cancels out.}

The ratio of the quantities of calcium in water (a) and water (b) is 117 : 30 or 3.9 : 1. {Recall that ratios do not have units; look back at Box 2.4 if you had difficulty with this question.}

{Note how much easier it is to read label (b) than label (a) because the information is laid out in columns in a table.}

Question 4.9   Water is taken in both in food and in drink and is lost from the body in sweat, in the air exhaled from the lungs, in faeces and in urine. {This can be written as a word equation.

water in food   =   water in sweat + water
+ water in drink   in exhaled air + water in
                         faeces + water in urine.}

Question 5.1   Words, or pairs of words, that begin with a capital letter are: Celsius (the name of the scientist who devised the Celsius scale), Sahara Desert, Arctic Circle (both the names of specific parts of the world), and Earth, when it applies to the name of our planet. Note, however, that when 'earth' is used to mean garden soil, then no capital letter is used. The word 'scale' in 'Celsius scale' does not have a capital letter, because it is not unique; there are many different scales. Similarly, barrel cactus, oxygen and desert (when the word is not part of the name of a place) do not begin with capital letters; there are millions of barrel cactus plants, countless billions of particles of oxygen and several different deserts.

Question 6.1   From Table 6.1, the volume of water stored in ice and snow is 43 000 000 km^3. Expressing this as a fraction of the total volume, we get

$$\dfrac{43\,000\,000 \text{ km}^3}{1\,460\,000\,000 \text{ km}^3}$$

We can cancel six zeros (and the unit) from the top and the bottom of this fraction, so the percentage is

$$\dfrac{43}{1460} \times 100\% - 2.9\%$$

{Note that 43 is exactly the same percentage of 1 460, as 43 000 000 is of 1 460 000 000.}

Question 6.2 (a) 1.0×10^8; (b) 4.0×10^{11}; (c) 3.5×10^4; (d) 9.5×10^6; (e) 5.1×10^2.

Question 6.3 (a) 73 000; (b) 3 600 000; (c) 444 000; (d) 6 050.

Question 6.4 1.46×10^{21}. There are two ways of doing this. Starting with 1.46, the decimal point has to be moved 21 places to the right to produce 1 460 000 000 000 000 000 000. Therefore, the power of ten must be 21. An alternative approach is to recognize that 1.46 has to be multiplied by 10 twenty-one times to obtain 1 460 000 000 000 000 000 000. Again, this tells us that the power term must be 10^{21}.

{Note that a quick way of counting up the zeros is to use the spaces between every three zeros, and count them in threes from the right.}

Question 6.5 The boxes should read as follows: oceans 1.4×10^9; ice and snow 4.3×10^7; underground water 1.5×10^7; lakes and rivers 3.6×10^5; atmosphere 1.5×10^4; plants and animals 2.0×10^3.

Question 6.6 (a) The starting point for quoting 0.000 000 000 25 in scientific notation is 2.5 (the number that lies between 1.0 and 9.9). The decimal point has to be moved ten places to the left to reach 0.000 000 000 25, so the power of ten must be -10 and the answer 2.5×10^{-10} m.

(b) 2.5×10^{-4} m.

(c) First of all you convert the fraction $\frac{1}{1\,000\,000}$ into a decimal. This is 0.000 001. In scientific notation this is 1×10^{-6} m. Alternatively, $\frac{1}{1\,000\,000}\,\text{m} = \frac{1}{10^6}\,\text{m}$

$= 10^{-6}$ m, since $\frac{1}{10^6} = 10^{-6}$.

(d) 3.5×10^{-3} m.

Question 6.7 (a) To find the decimal number corresponding to 7.3×10^{-4}, the decimal point in 7.3 has to be moved four places to the left to give 0.000 73. The alternative approach is to think of, and work out, $7.3 \div 10 \div 10 \div 10 \div 10$.

(b) 0.000 000 29.

Question 6.8 (a) From the definition of the prefixes, 1 km = 1 000 m and 1 m = 1 000 mm. So

1 km = 1 000 × 1 m = 1 000 × (1 000 mm)
= 1 000 000 mm = 10^6 mm

(b) Since 10^6 mm = 1 km, from part (a), then

$$1\,\text{mm} = \frac{1\,\text{km}}{10^6} = \frac{1}{10^6}\,\text{km} = 10^{-6}\,\text{km}$$

(c) In Section 6.1.1 you saw that 10 000 × 10 000 × 10 000 litres could be stacked in a one kilometre cube, so

1 km³ = 10 000 × 10 000 × 10 000 litres = 10^{12} litres.

Question 6.9 (a) The domestic use per person in developing countries is 10 litres per day, and that in the UK is 136 litres per day. As a percentage, this is:

$$\frac{10\,\text{litres per day}}{136\,\text{litres per day}} \times 100\% = 7.3529\%$$

or 7.4% when rounded to one decimal place.

(b) The water used for domestic purposes in the UK as a percentage of the total use is:

$$\frac{136\,\text{litres}}{604\,\text{litres}} \times 100\% = 22.51655\%$$

Rounding this to one decimal place gives 22.5%.

Question 6.10 The dissolved oxygen level at this point was about 25% of that at saturation. {If you didn't obtain this answer, then check by following the line vertically upwards from the 20 km downstream marker on the horizontal axis to the point where it meets the curve for 1893. Now draw a line horizontally across the page from this point to where it meets the vertical axis. This should be about half way between 20% and the next grid line (30%), i.e. 25%.}

Question 7.1 (a) $2^3 = 2 \times 2 \times 2 = 8$; (b) $3^2 = 3 \times 3 = 9$; (c) $2^5 = 2 \times 2 \times 2 \times 2 \times 2 = 32$; (d) $4^2 = 4 \times 4 = 16$.

Question 7.2 (a) $8 \times 8 \times 8 \times 8 = 8^4$; (b) $5 \times 5 = 5^2$; (c) $3 \times 3 \times 3 \times 3 \times 3 = 3^5$; (d) $m \times m \times m \times m = m^4$.

Question 7.3 (a) $2^{-1} = \frac{1}{2} = 0.5$

(b) $4^{-2} = \frac{1}{4 \times 4} = \frac{1}{16} = 0.0625$

(c) $5^{-3} = \frac{1}{5 \times 5 \times 5} = \frac{1}{125} = 0.008$

Question 7.4 (a) $\dfrac{1}{2 \times 2 \times 2 \times 2} = \dfrac{1}{2^4} = 2^{-4}$

(b) $1 \div 3 \div 3 \div 3 \div 3 \div 3 = \dfrac{1}{3 \times 3 \times 3 \times 3 \times 3} = \dfrac{1}{3^5} = 3^{-5}$

(c) $\dfrac{1}{m \times m} = \dfrac{1}{m^2} = m^{-2}$

Question 7.5 (a) kilograms per square metre = kg/m^2

$= \dfrac{kg}{m^2} = kg\,m^{-2}$. {Remember, 'per' means 'divide by' and square metres are metres × metres, or m^2.}

(b) metres per second = m/s = $\dfrac{m}{s}$ = m s^{-1}.

(c) milligrams per litre = mg/l = $\dfrac{mg}{l}$ = mg l^{-1}.

{Note how all of these units are written with a space between the units. Without the space (b), for example, would be ms^{-1}, i.e. per millisecond.}

Question 7.6 Fertilizers, intended to help grow healthier crops to feed more people, may end up depleting rivers and lakes of their oxygen, and killing the animals that live there. Industries manufacturing goods intended to raise our standard of living may discharge waste products into water, and it may only be discovered years later that these are toxic.

Acknowledgements

Grateful acknowledgement is made to the following sources for permission to reproduce material in this block:

Figures

Figures 2.1 and 2.2: © 1995 Comstock/George Gerster; *Figure 4.13*: Courtesy of the Royal Society of Chemistry; *Figure 4.1b*: From *Human Biology: Form, function and adaptation* by William DeWitt. Copyright © 1989 by Scott, Foresman. Reprinted by permission of Addison-Wesley Educational Publishers; *Figure 6.1*: Courtesy of NASA; *Figures 6.3a and b*: Courtesy of Dr Evelyn Brown; *Figures 6.3c and 6.6*: Still Pictures; *Figure 6.4*: Science Photo Library/Simon Fraser; *Figure 6.5*: Richardson Photography; *Figure 6.9*: Warner, Sir F. 1994, *Conference Paper No. 4, Industry and Society*, HRH The Duke of Edinburgh's Study Conference, July 1994.

Title page photographs

Camels: Ardea London Ltd; *Cacti*: Courtesy of Dr Colin Walker.

Index

Entries and page numbers in **bold type** refer to key words which are printed in **bold** in the text and which are defined in the Glossary. These are terms that we expect you to be able to explain the meaning of, and use correctly, both during and at the end of the course. An entry followed by G indicates a term which is defined in the Glossary but which is not bold in the text. Where the page number is given in *italics*, the indexed information is carried mainly or wholly in an illustration or table. Section summaries and answers to questions are not indexed.

S103 Course Team

S103 *Discovering Science* was produced for the Science Faculty by a team drawn from many areas of the Open University. The full list of contributors to the course is printed in the S103 *Course Guide*.

Block 1 was produced for the S103 Course Team by the team of people listed below.

Block Chair:	Judith Metcalfe (Biology)
Authors:	Evelyn Brown (Earth Sciences), Stuart Freake (Physics), Judith Metcalfe (Biology), Malcolm Rose (Chemistry)
Course Team Chair:	Stuart Freake
Course Manager:	Isla McTaggart
Editor:	Perry Morley
OU Graphic Design:	Sarah Crompton, Ruth Drage, Alison George, Howard Taylor
Centre for Educational Software:	Philip Butcher, Chris Denham, Jon Rosewell, Craig Wotherspoon
BBC/OUPC:	Phil Ashby, Tony Jolly, Paul Manners
External course assessor:	Prof. Paul Black (King's College, London)

The block has also benefited greatly from comments and other forms of help during its production from Audrey Brown (Associate Lecturer, AL), David Campbell (AL), Bob Cordell, Barrie Jones, Sally Jordan (AL), Clive Lawless (Institute of Educational Technology), Annie Payne, Helen Wood (AL) and all the students who tested materials.